RIFFS & RHYTHMS

CHARTBUSTERS

**UNIQUE, EASY TO FOLLOW FORMAT
OVER 40 MASSIVE ROCK & POP HITS
SPECIALLY PRESENTED FOR GUITARISTS**

WISE PUBLICATIONS
PART OF THE MUSIC SALES GROUP
LONDON / NEW YORK / PARIS / SYDNEY / COPENHAGEN / BERLIN / MADRID / TOKYO

CW00377134

PUBLISHED BY
WISE PUBLICATIONS
14-15 BERNERS STREET, LONDON W1T 3LJ, UK.

EXCLUSIVE DISTRIBUTORS:
MUSIC SALES LIMITED
DISTRIBUTION CENTRE, NEWMARKET ROAD, BURY ST EDMUNDS, SUFFOLK IP33 3YB, UK.
MUSIC SALES PTY LIMITED
120 ROTHSCHILD AVENUE, ROSEBERY, NSW 2018, AUSTRALIA.

ORDER NO. AM985160
ISBN 978-1-84609-471-2
THIS BOOK © COPYRIGHT 2007 WISE PUBLICATIONS, A DIVISION OF MUSIC SALES LIMITED.

EDITED BY DAVID HARRISON
COMPILED BY NICK CRISPIN
MUSIC ARRANGED BY MATT COWE
MUSIC PROCESSED BY PAUL EWERS MUSIC DESIGN
COVER DESIGNED BY FRESH LEMON
COVER PHOTOGRAPHS COURTESY OF LFI
PRINTED IN THE EU

YOUR GUARANTEE OF QUALITY
AS PUBLISHERS, WE STRIVE TO PRODUCE EVERY BOOK TO THE HIGHEST COMMERCIAL STANDARDS.
THE MUSIC HAS BEEN FRESHLY ENGRAVED AND THE BOOK HAS BEEN CAREFULLY DESIGNED
TO MINIMISE AWKWARD PAGE TURNS AND TO MAKE PLAYING FROM IT A REAL PLEASURE.
PARTICULAR CARE HAS BEEN GIVEN TO SPECIFYING ACID-FREE, NEUTRAL-SIZED
PAPER MADE FROM PULPS WHICH HAVE NOT BEEN ELEMENTAL CHLORINE BLEACHED.
THIS PULP IS FROM FARMED SUSTAINABLE FORESTS AND WAS PRODUCED WITH SPECIAL REGARD FOR
THE ENVIRONMENT. THROUGHOUT, THE PRINTING AND BINDING HAVE BEEN PLANNED TO ENSURE A STURDY,
ATTRACTIVE PUBLICATION WHICH SHOULD GIVE YEARS OF ENJOYMENT.
IF YOUR COPY FAILS TO MEET OUR HIGH STANDARDS, PLEASE INFORM US AND WE WILL GLADLY REPLACE IT.

WWW.MUSICROOM.COM

CIGARETTES & ALCOHOL

Words & Music by Noel Gallagher

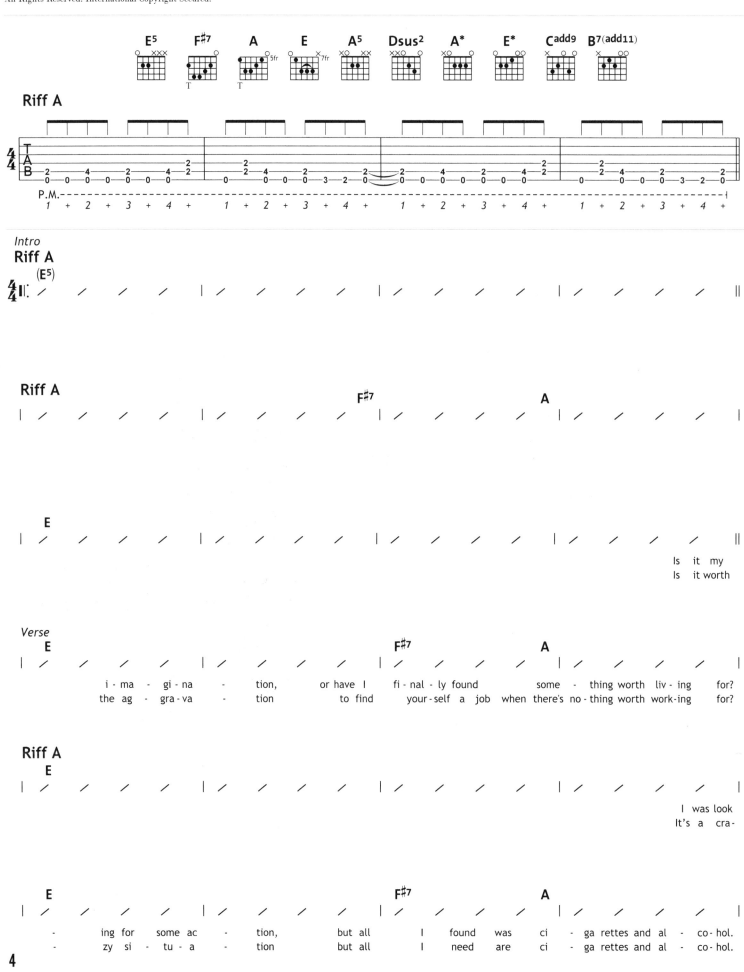

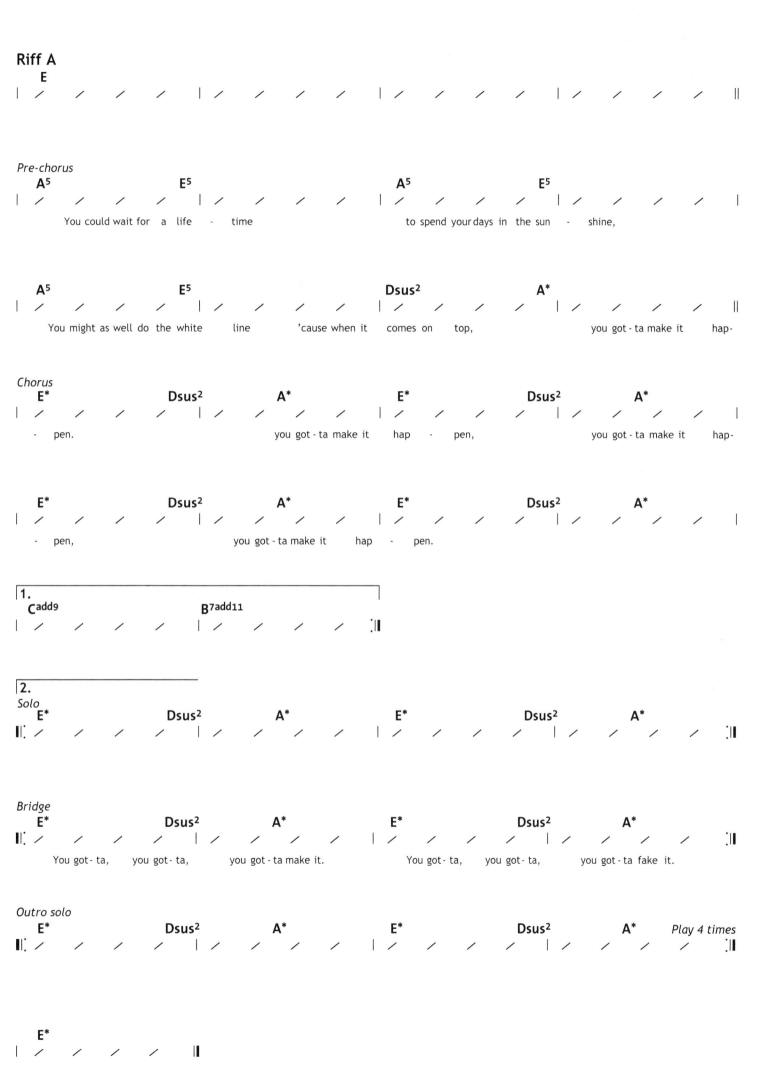

Riff A

Pre-chorus

You could wait for a life - time to spend your days in the sun - shine,

You might as well do the white line 'cause when it comes on top, you got - ta make it hap-

Chorus

- pen. you got - ta make it hap - pen, you got - ta make it hap-

- pen, you got - ta make it hap - pen.

1.

2.

Solo

Bridge

You got - ta, you got - ta, you got - ta make it. You got - ta, you got - ta, you got - ta fake it.

Outro solo

Play 4 times

DOWN DOWN

Words & Music by Robert Young & Francis Rossi

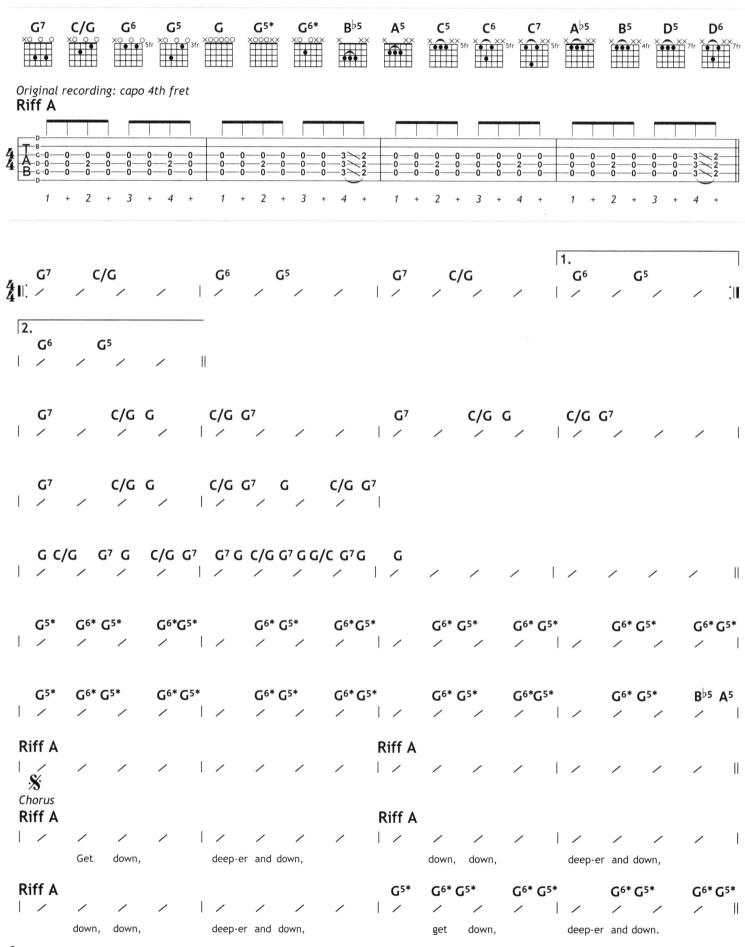

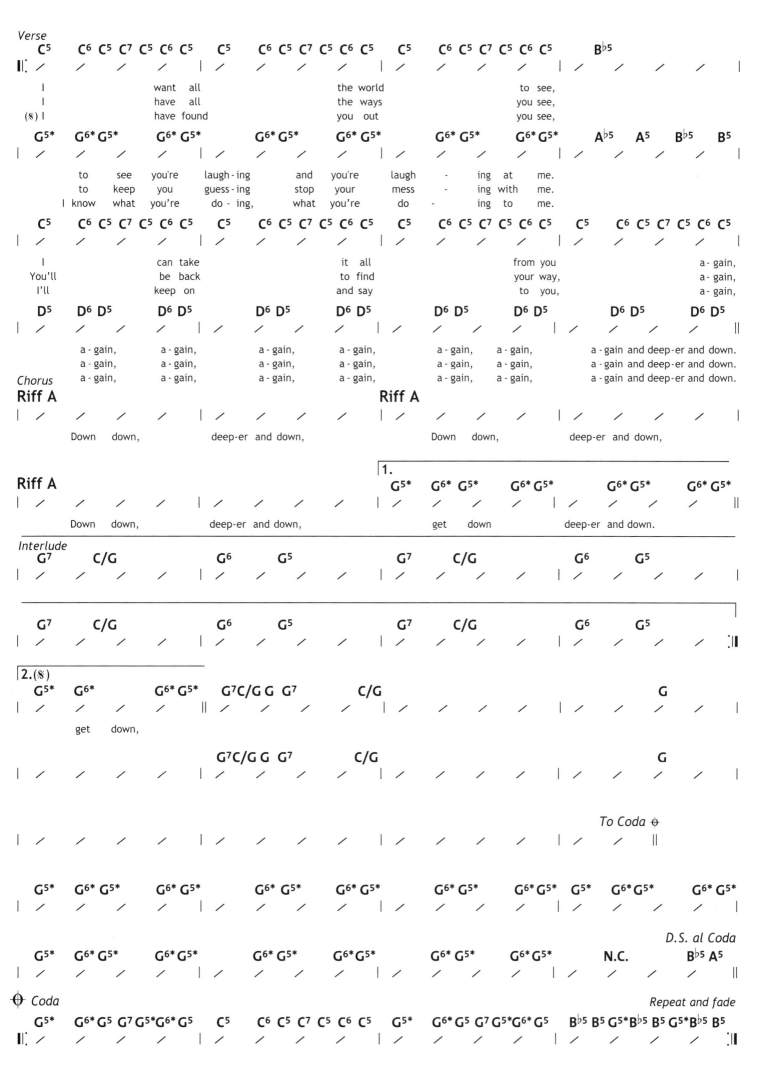

ELEVATION

Words by Bono
Music by U2

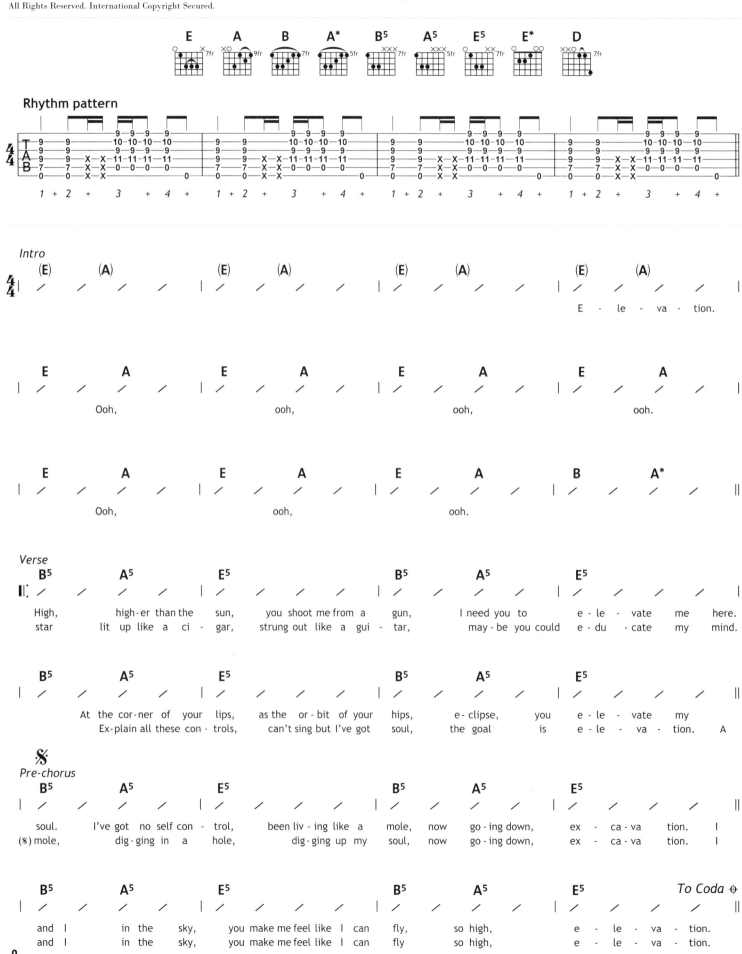

Chorus

| E | A | | E | A | | E | A | | **1.** B | A* :||

Ooh,   ooh,   ooh.   el - e - va - tion! A

2.

| E | A | ||

Ooh,

| E | A | | E | A | | E | A | | B | A* ||

ooh,   ooh,   ooh.   E - le - va - tion.

Bridge

| E* | | A* | |

Love   live me   out   from   of   these   blues,   won't you

| E* | D | | A* |

tell   me   some - thing   true,   I   be - lieve   in   you.

D.S. al Coda

| |

⊕ *Coda*

| N.C.(E) (E♭) (D) | (E) (E♭) (D) |

| (E) (E♭) (D) (D♭) | (C) (B) A* ||

E - le - va - tion.

1.

|| E | A | | E | A | | E | A | | E | A :||

Ooh,   ooh,   ooh,   ooh.

2.

| B | A* | E* ||

E - le - va - tion.

(EVERYTHING I DO) I DO IT FOR YOU

Words by Bryan Adams & Robert John Lange
Music by Michael Kamen

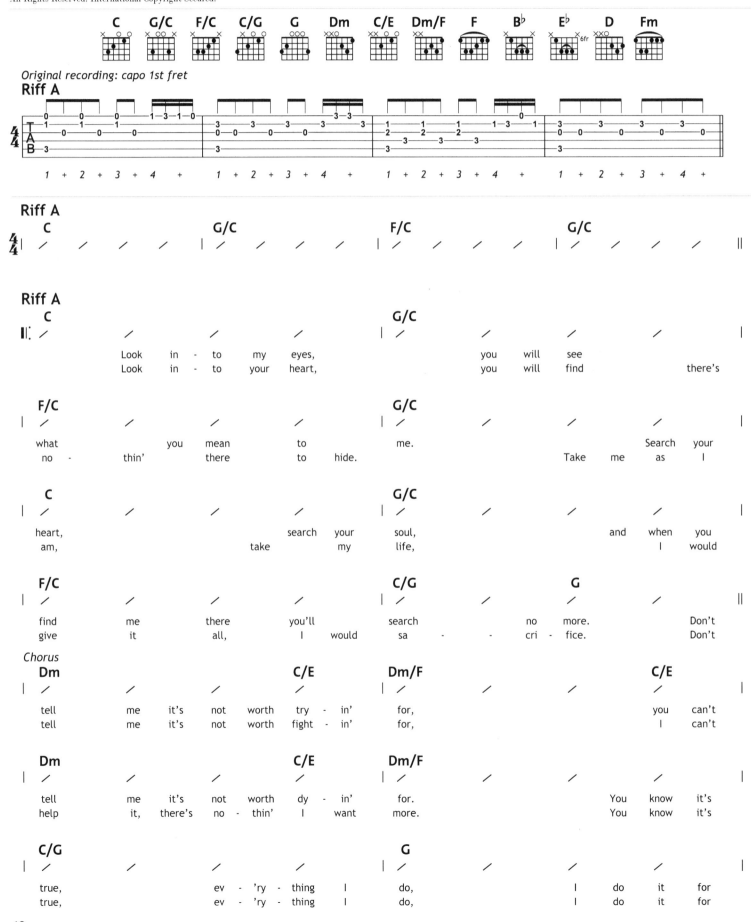

1. C

/ / / / | / / / / :‖

you.

2. C

/ / / / | / / / / ‖

you.   There's

Bridge

B♭   E♭   B♭   F

/ / / / | / / / / | / / / / | / / / / |

no   love   like   your   love   and   no   oth - er   could   give   more   love.   There's

C   G   D   G

/ / / / | / / / / | / / / / | / / / / |

no - where,   un - less   you're   there   all   the   time,   all   the   way.   Yeah.

N.C.

/ / / / ‖

Guitar solo

F   C

/ / / / | / / / / | / / / / | / / / / |

F   C

/ / / / | / / / / | / / / / | / / / / ‖

Oh,   you   can't

Chorus

Dm   G   Dm   G

/ / / / | / / / / | / / / / | / / / / |

tell   me   it's   not   worth   try - in'   for,   I   can't   help   it,   there's   no - thin'   I   want   more.   Yeah,   I   would

C   G   F   Fm

/ / / / | / / / / | / / / / | / / / / |

fight   for   you,   I'd   lie   for   you,   walk   the   wire   for   you,   yeah   I'd   die   for   you.

C/G   G   F

/ / / / | / / / / | / / / / | / / / / |

You   know   it's   true,   ev -'ry - thing   I   do,   oh,   I   do   it   for

C   N.C.

/ / / / | / / / / ‖

you.

Outro (ad lib. vox)

F   C

‖: / / / / | / / / / | / / / / | / / / / |

F   C   *Play 5 times and fade*

/ / / / | / / / / | / / / / | / / / / :‖

GIRLS ON FILM

Words & Music by Duran Duran

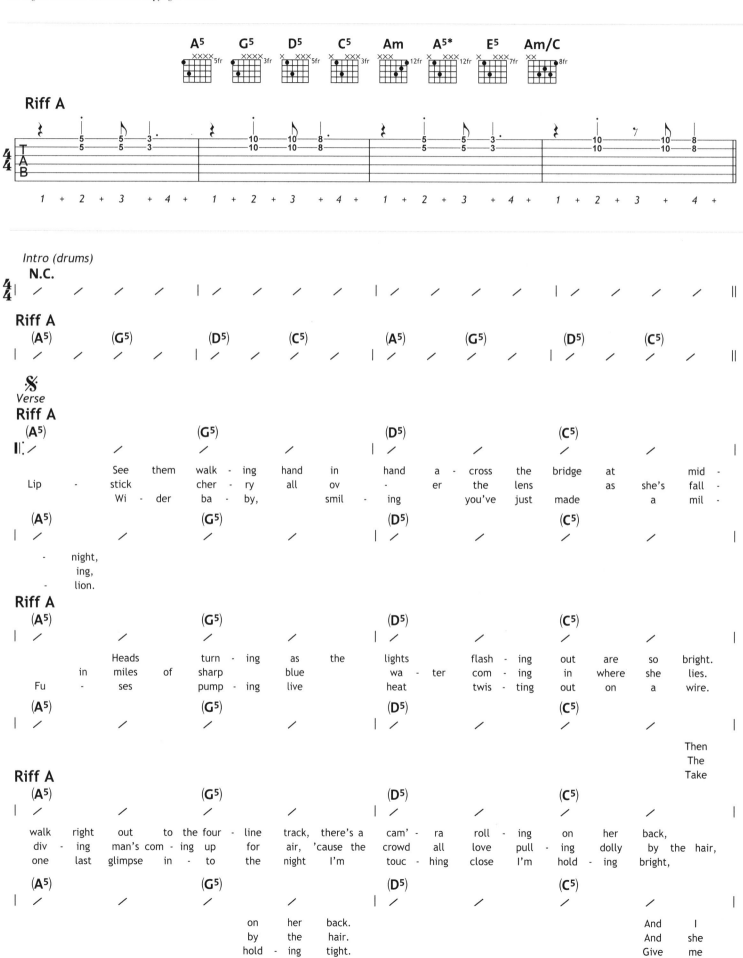

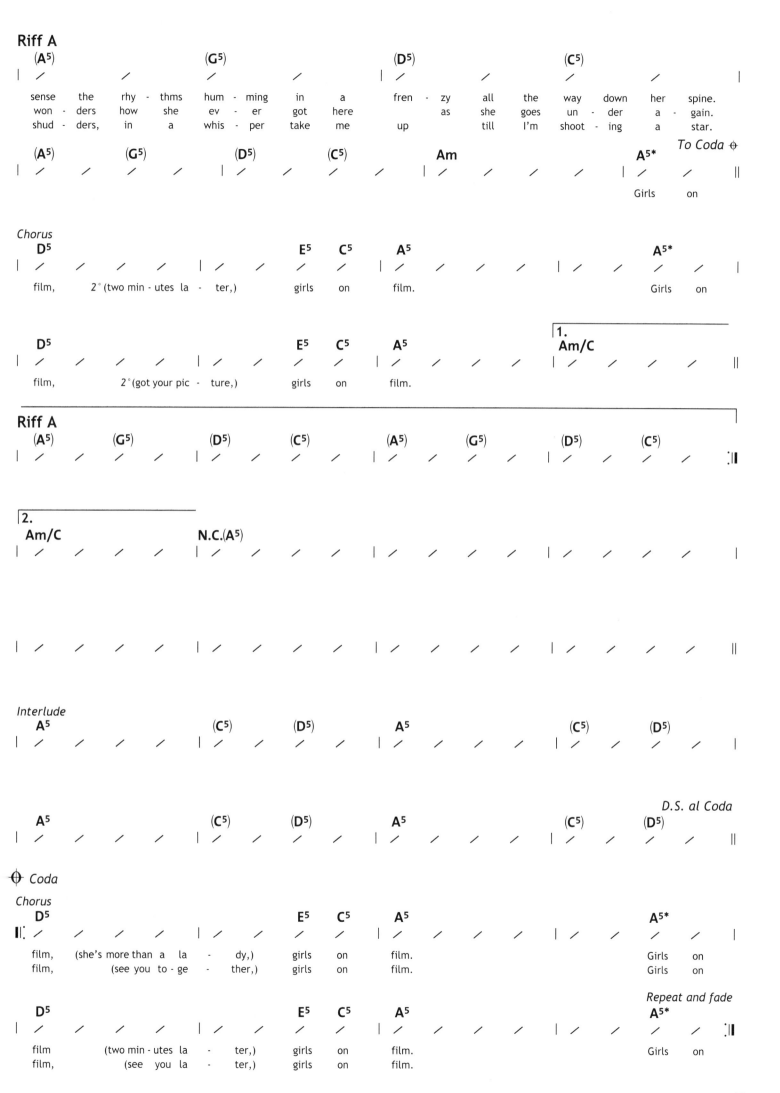

Riff A

(A⁵)   (G⁵)   (D⁵)   (C⁵)

sense   the   rhy - thms   hum - ming   in   a   fren - zy   all   the   way   down   her   spine.
won - ders   how   she   ev - er   got   here   as   she   goes   un - der   a - gain.
shud - ders,   in   a   whis - per   take   me   up   till   I'm   shoot - ing   a   star.

(A⁵)   (G⁵)   (D⁵)   (C⁵)   Am   *To Coda* ⊕   A⁵*

Girls   on

Chorus

D⁵   E⁵   C⁵   A⁵   A⁵*

film,   2°(two min - utes la - ter,)   girls   on   film.   Girls   on

1.

D⁵   E⁵   C⁵   A⁵   Am/C

film,   2°(got your pic - ture,)   girls   on   film.

Riff A

(A⁵)   (G⁵)   (D⁵)   (C⁵)   (A⁵)   (G⁵)   (D⁵)   (C⁵)

2.

Am/C   N.C.(A⁵)

Interlude

A⁵   (C⁵)   (D⁵)   A⁵   (C⁵)   (D⁵)

A⁵   (C⁵)   (D⁵)   A⁵   *D.S. al Coda*   (C⁵)   (D⁵)

⊕ *Coda*

Chorus

D⁵   E⁵   C⁵   A⁵   A⁵*

film,   (she's more than a la - dy,)   girls   on   film.   Girls   on
film,   (see you to - ge - ther,)   girls   on   film.   Girls   on

Repeat and fade

D⁵   E⁵   C⁵   A⁵   A⁵*

film   (two min - utes la - ter,)   girls   on   film.   Girls   on
film,   (see you la - ter,)   girls   on   film.

GOLD

Words & Music by Gary Kemp

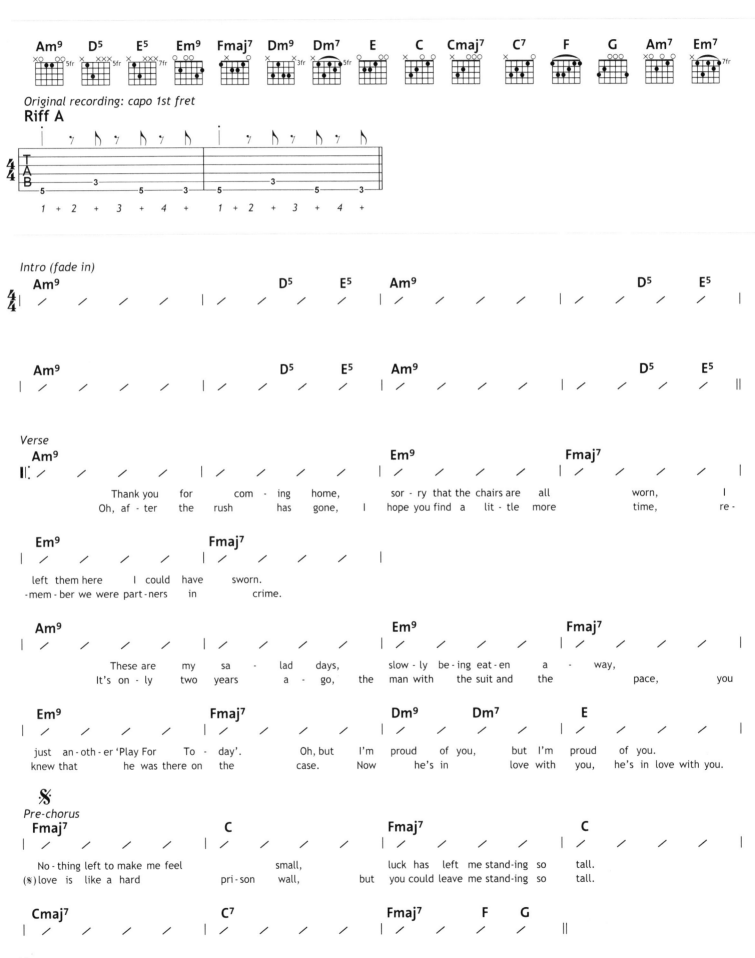

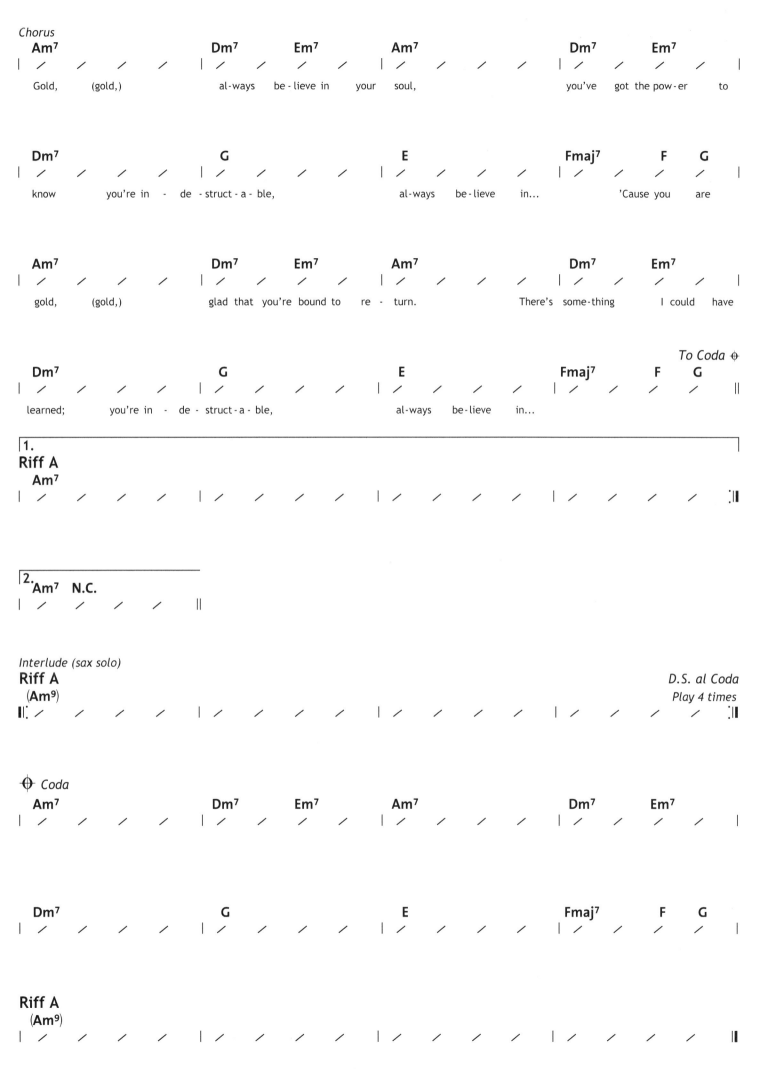

GOOD VIBRATIONS

Words & Music by Brian Wilson & Mike Love

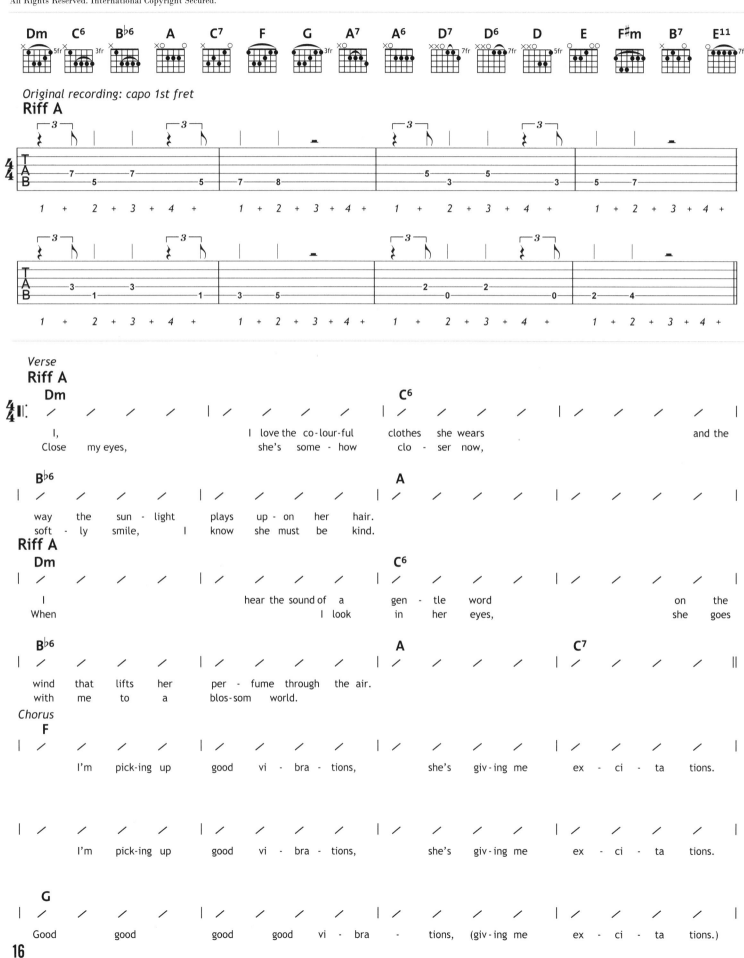

A

| / / / / | / / / / | / / / / | / / / / |

Good   good   good   good   vi - bra -   tions, (giv - ing me   ex - ci - ta   tions.)

Interlude

A⁷   **A⁶**   **A**   **A⁶**   **A⁷**   **A⁶**   **A**   **A⁶**

| / / / / | / / / / | / / / / | / / / / |

(-ta - tions.)

A⁷   **A⁶**   **A**   **A⁶**   **A⁷**   **A⁶**   **A**   **A⁶**

| / / / / | / / / / | / / / / | / / / / |

A⁷   **A⁶**   **A**   **A⁶**   **A⁷**   **A⁶**   **A**   **A⁶**

| / / / / | / / / / | / / / / | / / / / |

Ah,   Ah,   my,   my,   what   e - la -

D⁷   **D⁶**   **D**   **D⁶**   **D⁷**   **D⁶**   **D**   **D⁶**

| / / / / | / / / / | / / / / | / / / / |

don't know where   but she sends   me   there.

tion.)   (Ah,   my,   my,   what a sen - sa -

A⁷   **A⁶**   **A**   **A⁶**   **A⁷**   **A⁶**   **A**   **A⁶**

| / / / / | / / / / | / / / / | / / / ‖

(Ah,   my,   my,   what e - la -   tions.)

- tion.)   (Ah,   my,   my,   what.

Bridge

E   **F♯m**   **B⁷**

| / / / / | / / / / | / / / / | / / / ‖

E   **F♯m**   **B⁷**   *Play 3 times*

‖: / / / / | / / / / | / / / / | / / / :‖

Got   - ta keep   those   lov - in' good   vi - bra - tions a - hap pen-ing   with her.

E   **F♯m**   **B⁷**

| / / / / | / / / / | / / / / | / / / / |

E   **E¹¹**

| / / / / | / / / / | / / / / | / / / ‖

Ah.

Chorus

A

| / / / / | / / / / | / / / / | / / / / |

Good,   good,   good,   good vi - bra -   tions. (giv - ing me   ex - ci - ta - tions.)

G

| / / / / | / / / / | / / / / | / / / / |

Good,   good,   good,   good vi - bra -   tions.

F

| / / / / | / / / / ‖

Outro

F   **G**

| / / / / | / / / / | / / / / | / / / / |

Na na na na na,   na na na.   Na na na na na,   na na na,

A   **G**

| / / / / | / / / / | / / / / | / / / ‖

Do do do do do,   do do do.   Do do do do do,   do do do.

G

‖: / / / / | / / / / :‖

THE HOUSE OF THE RISING SUN

Traditional
Arranged by Alan Price

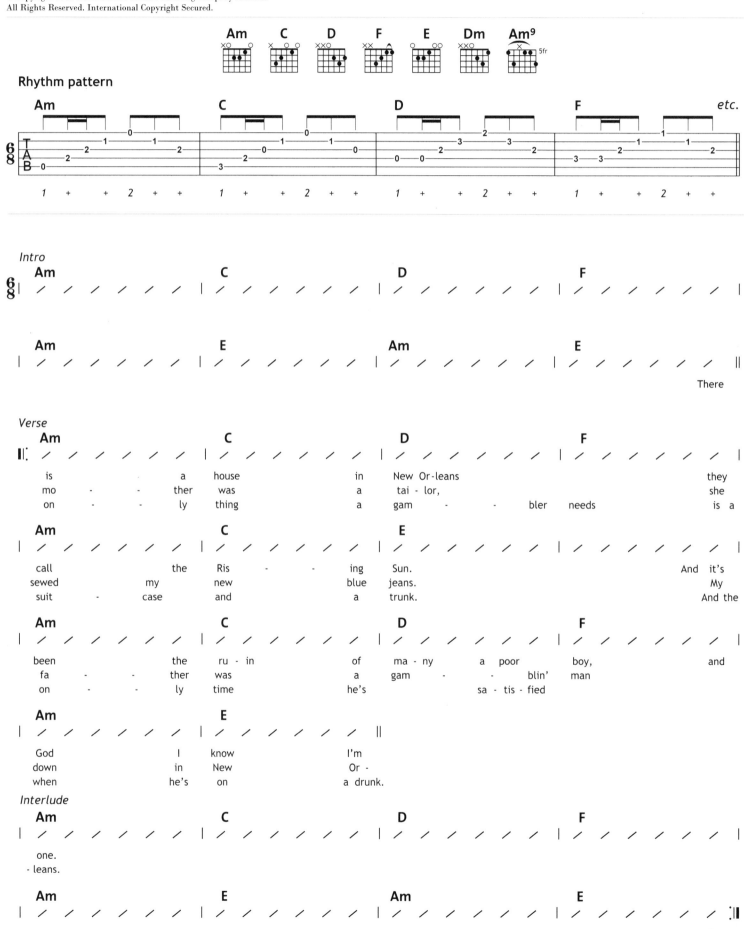

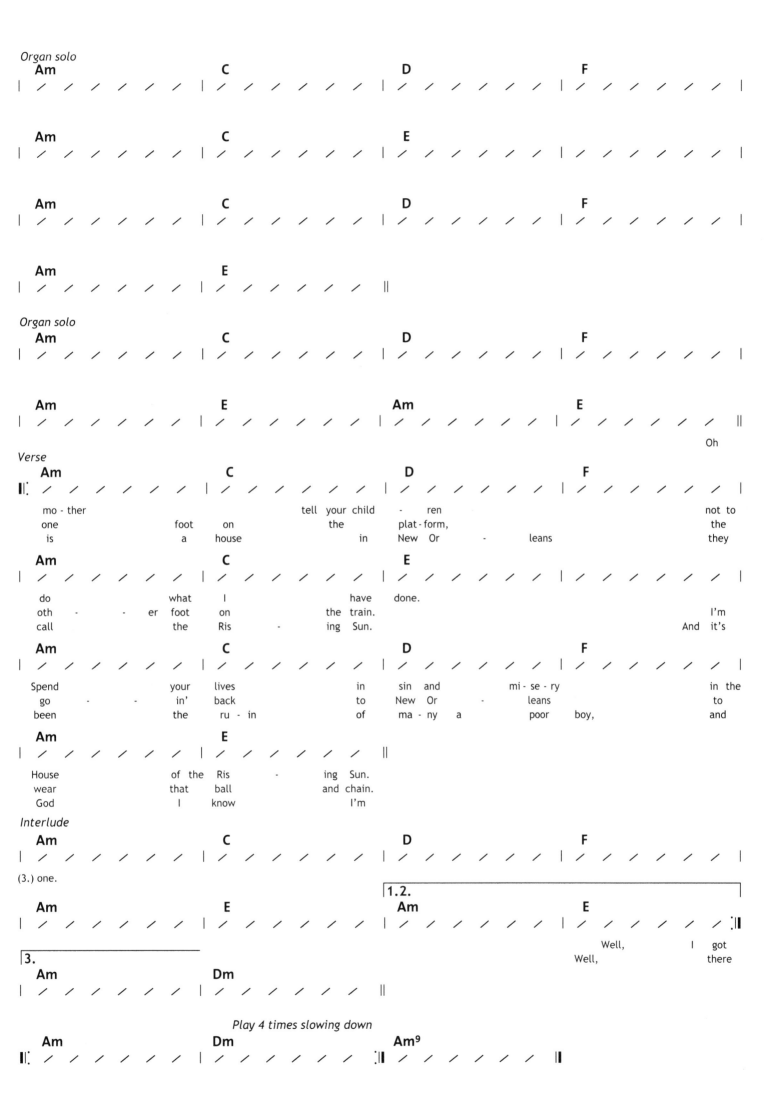

HURT

Words & Music by Trent Reznor

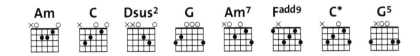

Am C Dsus² G Am⁷ Fadd⁹ C* G⁵

Rhythm pattern

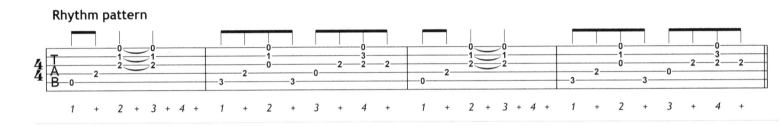

Intro

Am   C   Dsus²   Am   C   Dsus²

Verse

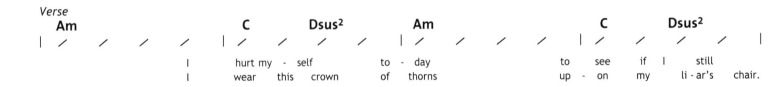

Am   C   Dsus²   Am   C   Dsus²

    I   hurt my - self   to - day   to see if I still

    I   wear this crown of thorns   up - on my li - ar's chair.

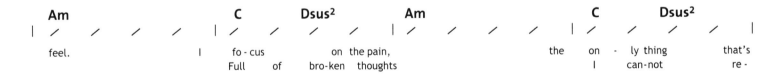

Am   C   Dsus²   Am   C   Dsus²

feel.   I fo - cus   on the pain,   the on - ly thing that's

        Full of bro - ken thoughts   I can - not   re -

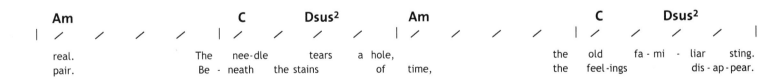

Am   C   Dsus²   Am   C   Dsus²

real.   The nee - dle tears a hole,   the old fa - mi - liar sting.

pair.   Be - neath the stains of time,   the feel - ings dis - ap - pear.

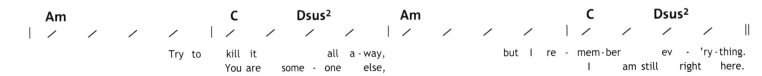

Am   C   Dsus²   Am   C   Dsus²

Try to kill it   all a - way,   but I re - mem - ber ev - 'ry - thing.

You are some - one else,   I am still right here.

Chorus

G   Am⁷   Fadd9   C*

What have   I   be-come,   my   sweet-est   friend?

G   Am⁷   Fadd9   C*

Ev-'ry - one   I   know   goes   a - way   in   the end.

G   Am⁷   Fadd9   G⁵

And   you   could have   it   all,   my   em - pire   of dirt.

G⁵   Am⁷   Fadd9   G⁵

I   will let   you   down,   I   will make   you   hurt.

Outro

G⁵   Am⁷   Fadd9   G⁵

If   I could   start   a - gain,   a   mil-lion   miles   a - way,

G⁵   Am⁷   Fadd9   G⁵

I would   keep   my - self,   I would   find

N.C.

a way.

IRONIC

Words by Alanis Morissette
Music by Alanis Morissette & Glen Ballard

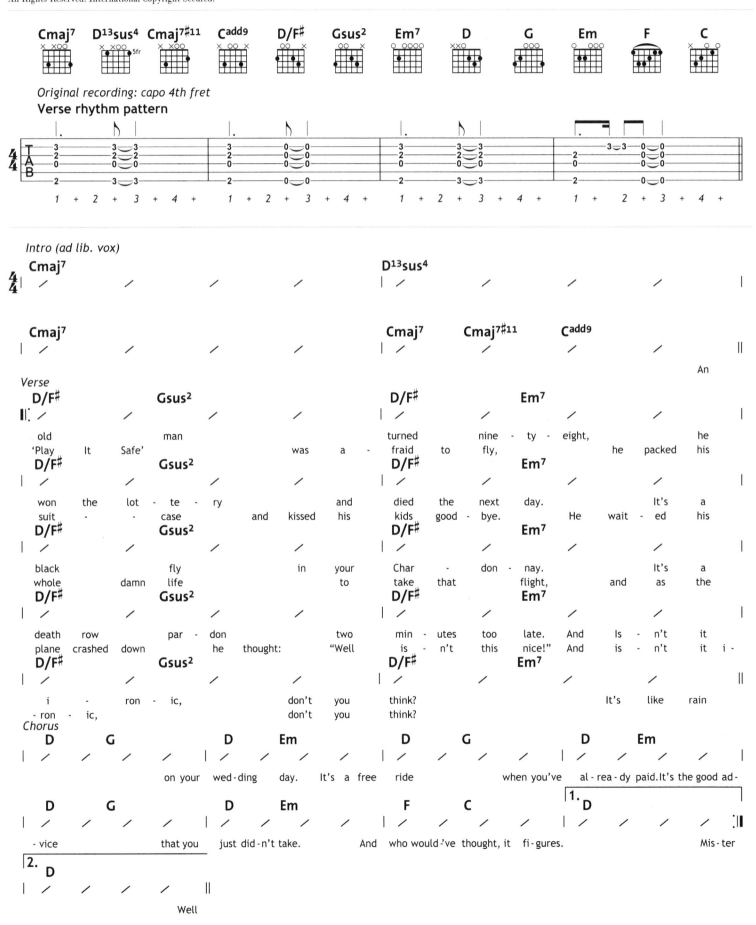

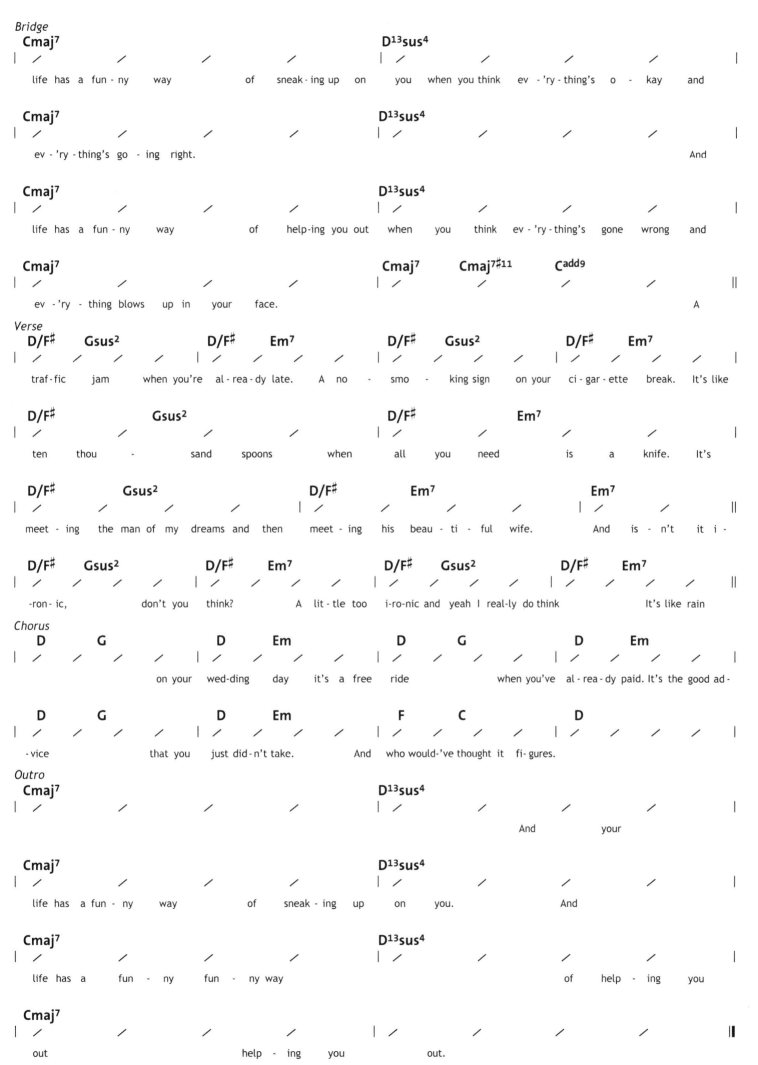

I SHOT THE SHERIFF

Words & Music by Bob Marley

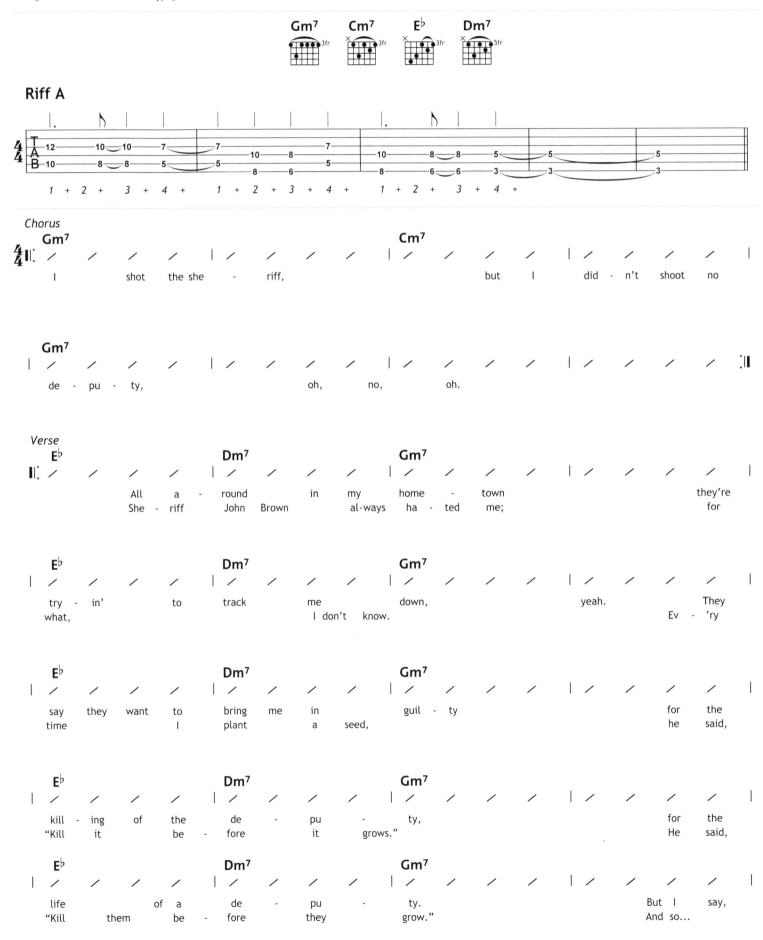

Riff A

N.C.

| ╱ ╱ ╱ ╱ | ╱ ╱ ╱ ╱ | ╱ ╱ ╱ ╱ | ╱ ╱ ╱ ╱ |

oh, now, now.

And so...

| ╱ ╱ ╱ ╱ ‖

Oh,
Read it   in   the news.

Chorus

Gm⁷   Cm⁷

| ╱ ╱ ╱ ╱ | ╱ ╱ ╱ ╱ | ╱ ╱ ╱ ╱ | ╱ ╱ ╱ ╱ |

I   shot the she - riff,   but I   swear it   was   in
I   shot the she - riff,   but I   swear it   was   in

Gm⁷

| ╱ ╱ ╱ ╱ | ╱ ╱ ╱ ╱ | ╱ ╱ ╱ ╱ | ╱ ╱ ╱ ╱ |

self - de - fence.   Ooh,   ooh,   ooh.   I said,
self - de - fence.   Ooh,   ooh,   ooh.   I said,

Gm⁷   Cm⁷

| ╱ ╱ ╱ ╱ | ╱ ╱ ╱ ╱ | ╱ ╱ ╱ ╱ | ╱ ╱ ╱ ╱ |

I   shot the she - riff,   oh, Lord,   and they say it   is   a
I   shot the she - riff,   but I   swear it   was in

Gm⁷

| ╱ ╱ ╱ ╱ | ╱ ╱ ╱ ╱ | ╱ ╱ ╱ ╱ | ╱ ╱ ╱ ╱ ‖

ca - pi - tal of - fence.   Ooh,   ooh,   ooh.   Hear this:
self - de - fence.   Yeah.   Ooh.

𝄋
Verse

E♭   Dm⁷   Gm⁷

| ╱ ╱ ╱ ╱ | ╱ ╱ ╱ ╱ | ╱ ╱ ╱ ╱ | ╱ ╱ ╱ ╱ |

Free - dom came my   way   one   day   and   I
-flex - es had the bet - ter of me   And

E♭   Dm⁷   Gm⁷

| ╱ ╱ ╱ ╱ | ╱ ╱ ╱ ╱ | ╱ ╱ ╱ ╱ | ╱ ╱ ╱ ╱ |

start - ed   out   of town,   yeah!
what is   to   be   must   be.   Ev -'ry

E♭   Dm⁷   Gm⁷

| ╱ ╱ ╱ ╱ | ╱ ╱ ╱ ╱ | ╱ ╱ ╱ ╱ | ╱ ╱ ╱ ╱ |

day   All of a   sud-den   I   saw   She-riff John Brown,
day   the buck - et a - go a   well;

E♭   Dm⁷   Gm⁷

| ╱ ╱ ╱ ╱ | ╱ ╱ ╱ ╱ | ╱ ╱ ╱ ╱ | ╱ ╱ ╱ ╱ |

aim - in' to shoot   me   down.   So,   I
one day   the bot - tom a - go drop out.

25

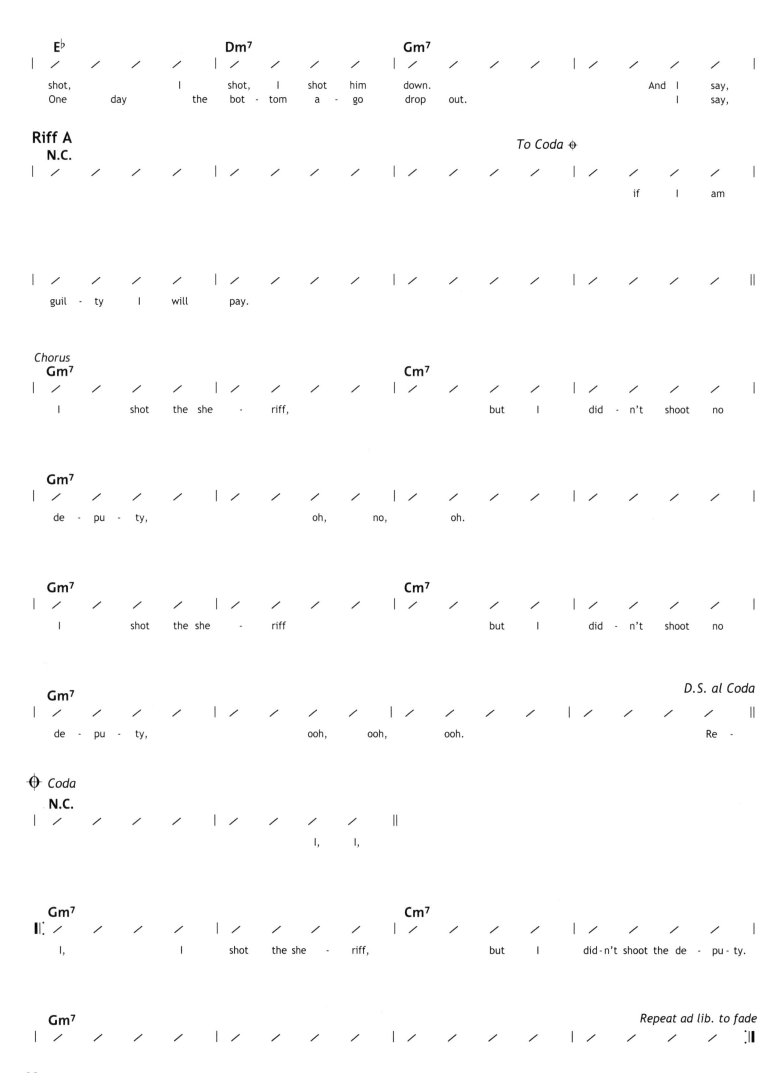

E♭　　　　　　　　**Dm⁷**　　　　　　　　**Gm⁷**

shot,　　　　　　I　shot, I　shot him　down.　　　　　　　　　　And I　say,
One　day　　the　bot - tom　a - go　drop　out.　　　　　　　　　　I　say,

Riff A
N.C.　　　　　　　　　　　　　　　　　　　*To Coda* ⊕

　　　　　　　　　　　　　　　　　　　　　　　　if　I　am

guil - ty　I　will　pay.

Chorus
Gm⁷　　　　　　　　　　　　　　　**Cm⁷**

I　　shot　the she - riff,　　　　　　but　I　did - n't shoot　no

Gm⁷

de - pu - ty,　　　　oh,　no,　oh.

Gm⁷　　　　　　　　　　　　　　　**Cm⁷**

I　　shot　the she - riff　　　　　　but　I　did - n't shoot　no

　　　　　　　　　　　　　　　　　　　D.S. al Coda

Gm⁷

de - pu - ty,　　　　ooh,　ooh,　ooh.　　　　　　Re -

⊕ *Coda*
N.C.

I,　　I,

Gm⁷　　　　　　　　　　　　　　　**Cm⁷**

I,　　　　I　shot　the she - riff,　　　　but　I　did - n't shoot the de - pu - ty.

　　　　　　　　　　　　　　　　Repeat ad lib. to fade
Gm⁷

26

IF IT MAKES YOU HAPPY

Words & Music by Sheryl Crow & Jeffrey Trott

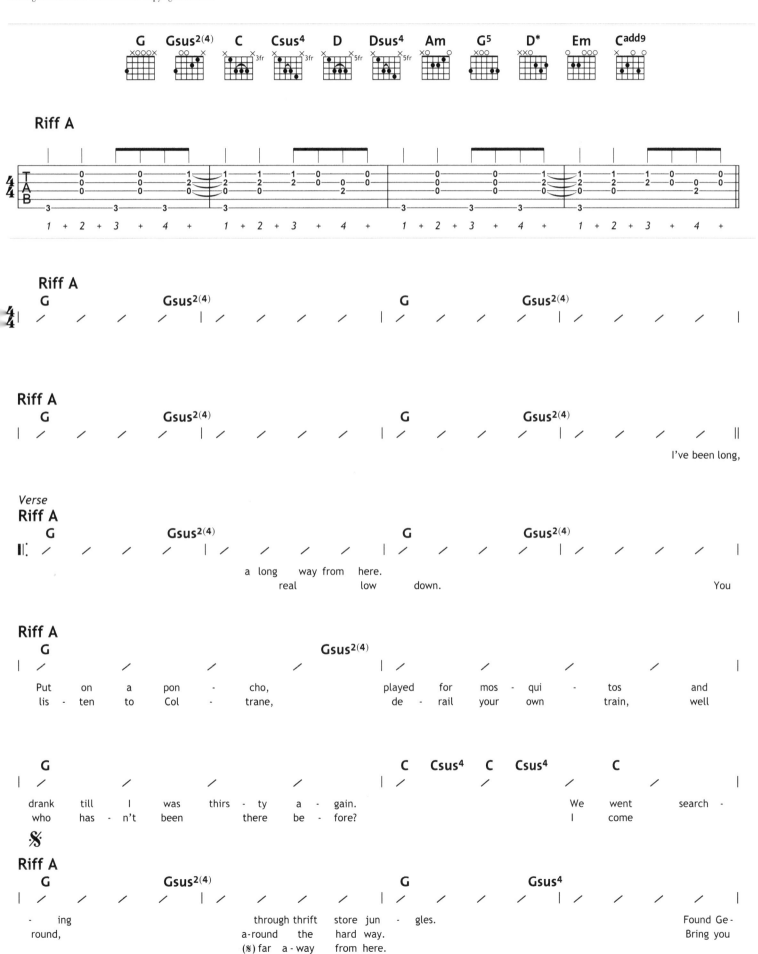

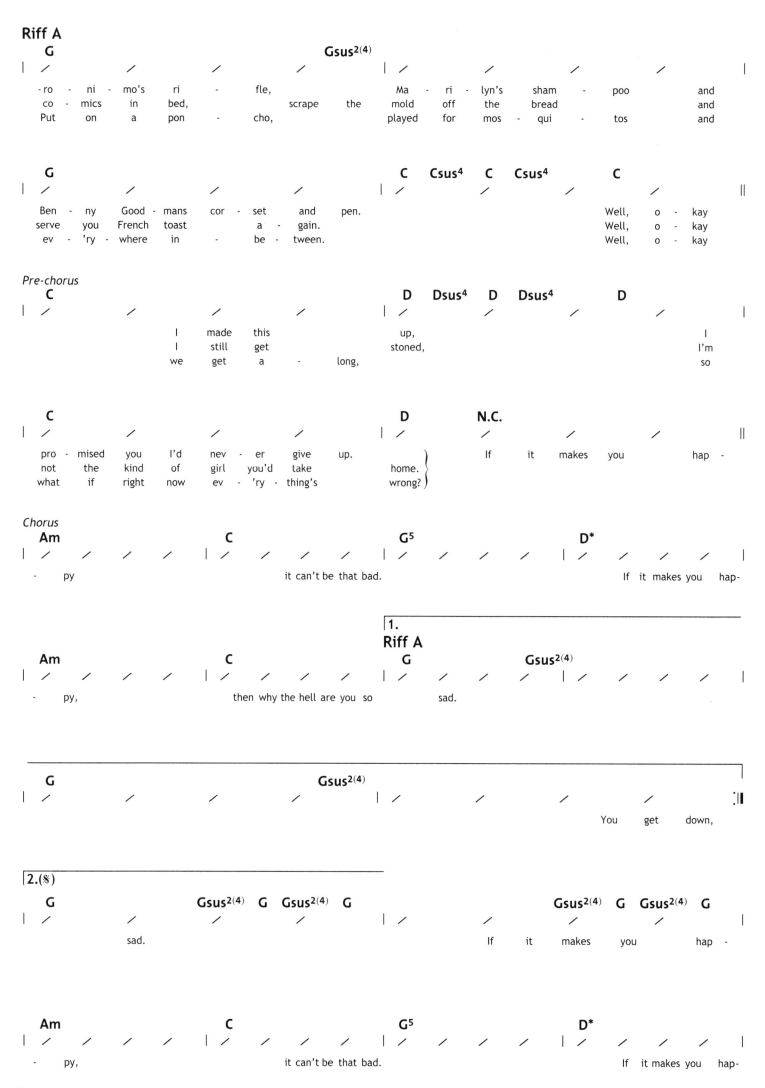

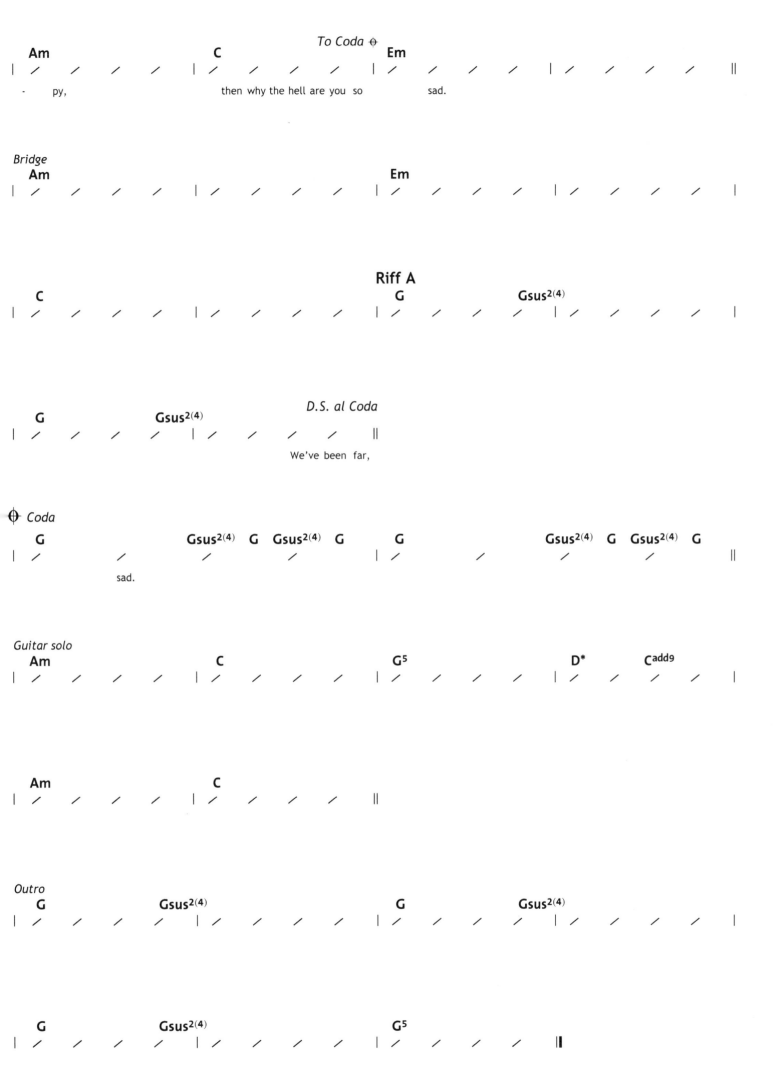

To Coda ⊕

Am / / / / | **C** / / / / | **Em** / / / / | / / / / ‖

- py,   then why the hell are you so   sad.

Bridge

Am / / / / | / / / / | **Em** / / / / | / / / / |

Riff A

C / / / / | / / / / | **G** / / / / **Gsus²⁽⁴⁾** | / / / / |

D.S. al Coda

G / / / **Gsus²⁽⁴⁾** / | / / / ‖

We've been far,

⊕ *Coda*

G / **Gsus²⁽⁴⁾ G Gsus²⁽⁴⁾ G** / **G** / | / / | **Gsus²⁽⁴⁾ G Gsus²⁽⁴⁾ G** / / ‖

sad.

Guitar solo

Am / / / / | **C** / / / / | **G⁵** / / / / | **D*** / / **Cᵃᵈᵈ⁹** / |

Am / / / / | **C** / / / / ‖

Outro

G / / / **Gsus²⁽⁴⁾** / | / / / | **G** / / / **Gsus²⁽⁴⁾** / | / / / |

G / / / **Gsus²⁽⁴⁾** / | / / / **G⁵** / / / ‖

THE JOKER

Words & Music by Steve Miller, Eddie Curtis & Ahmet Ertegun

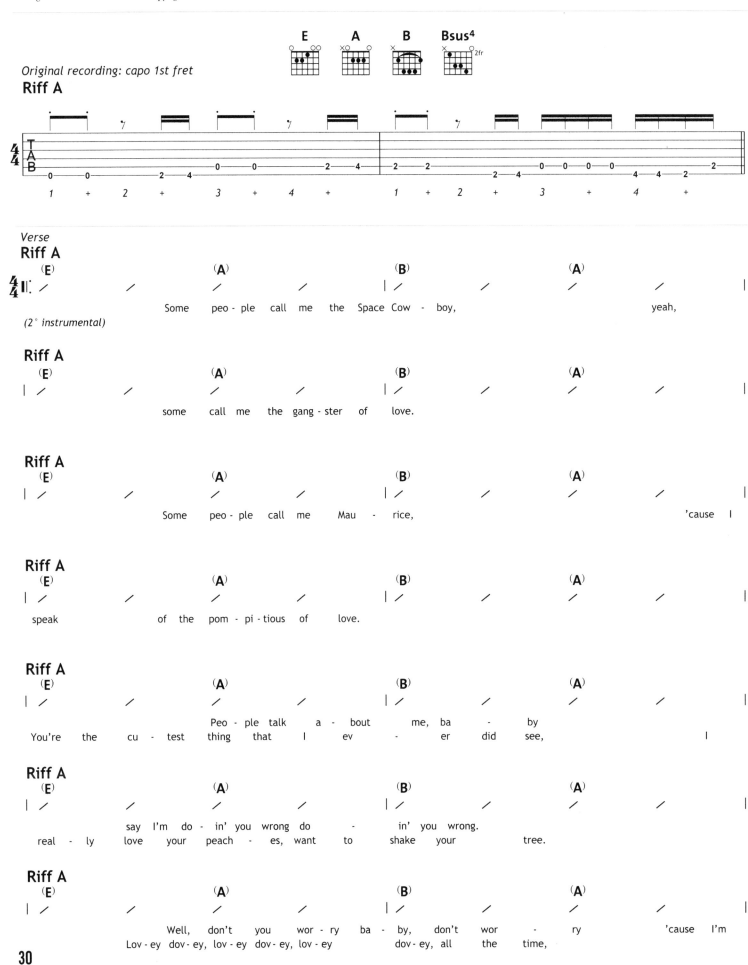

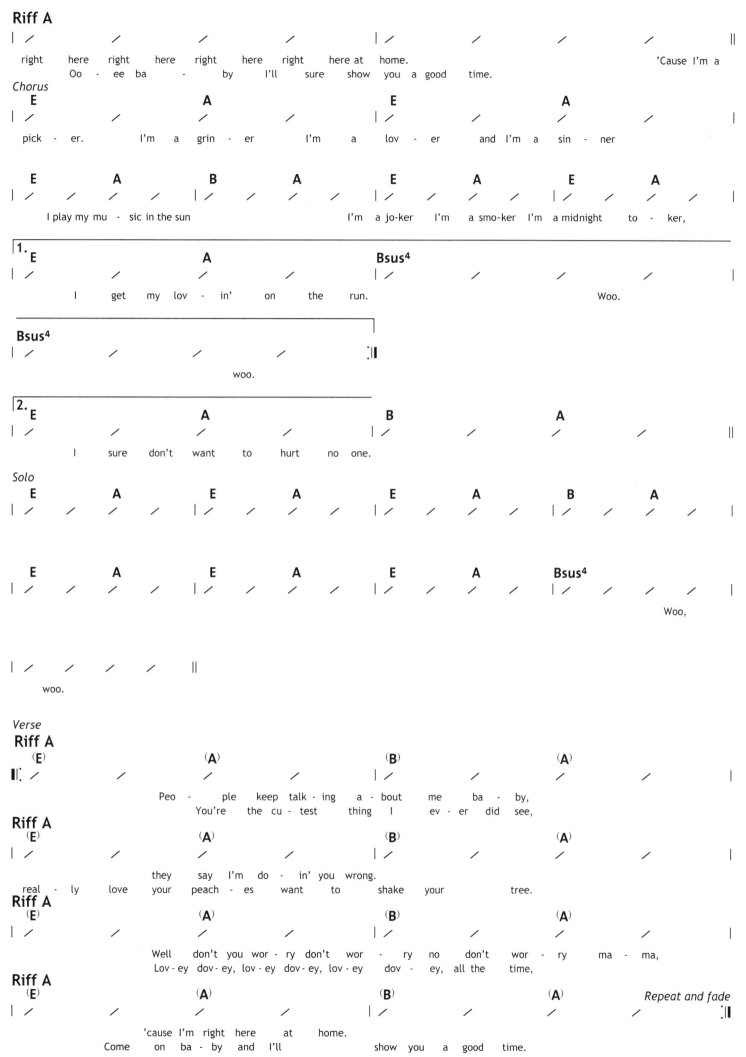

KILLING ME SOFTLY WITH HIS SONG

Words by Norman Gimbel
Music by Charles Fox

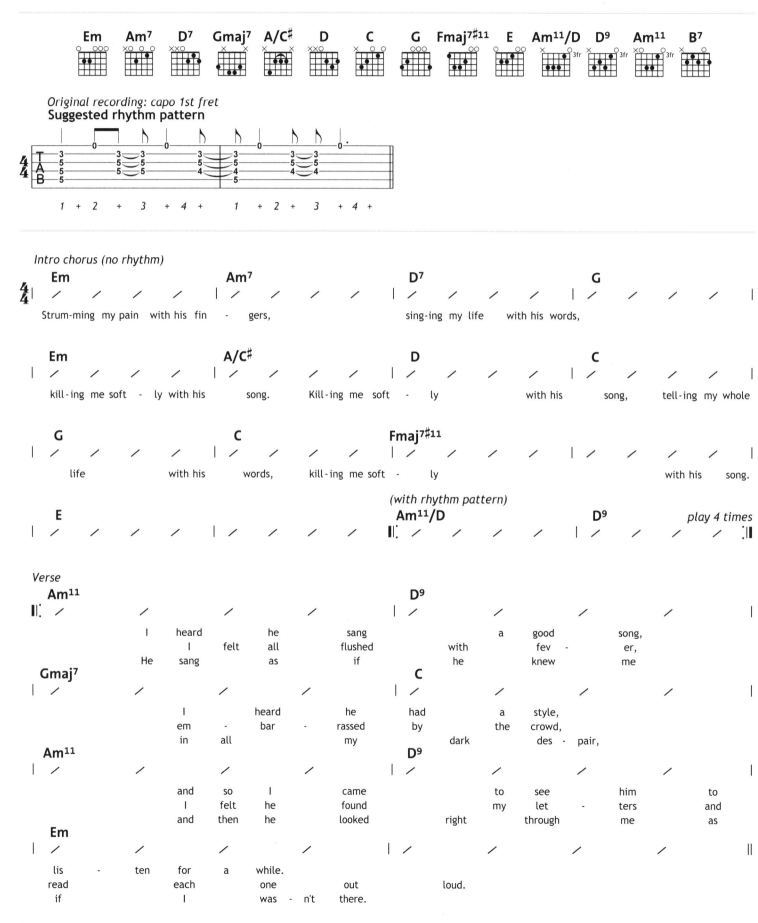

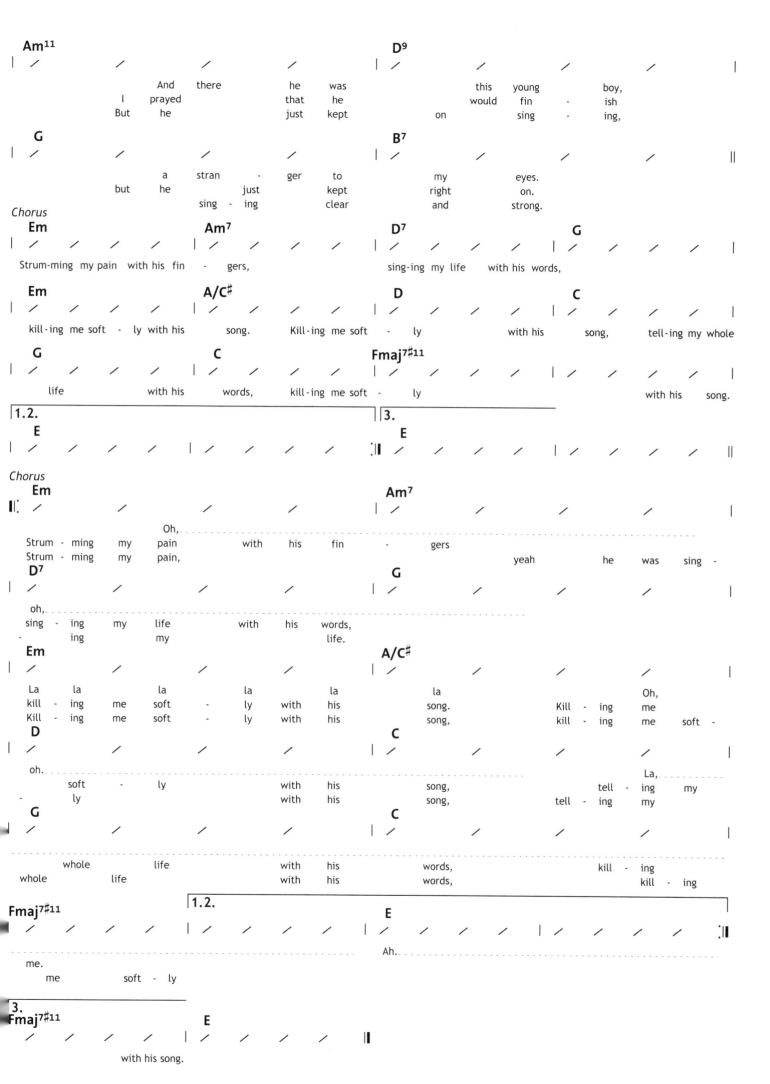

LIVIN' ON A PRAYER

Words & Music by Richie Sambora, Desmond Child & Jon Bon Jovi

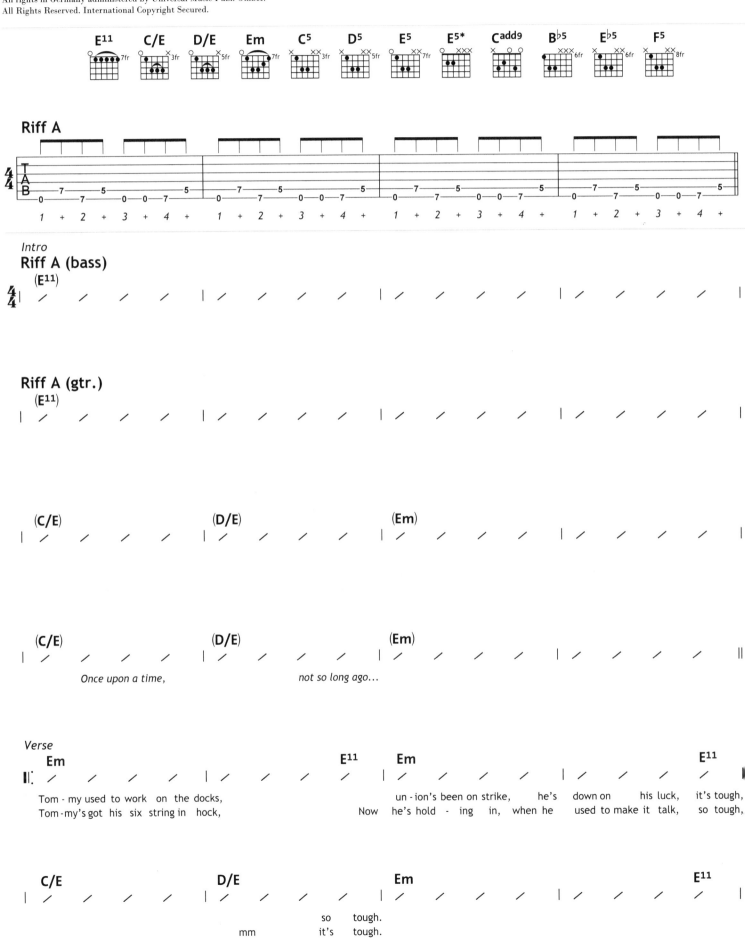

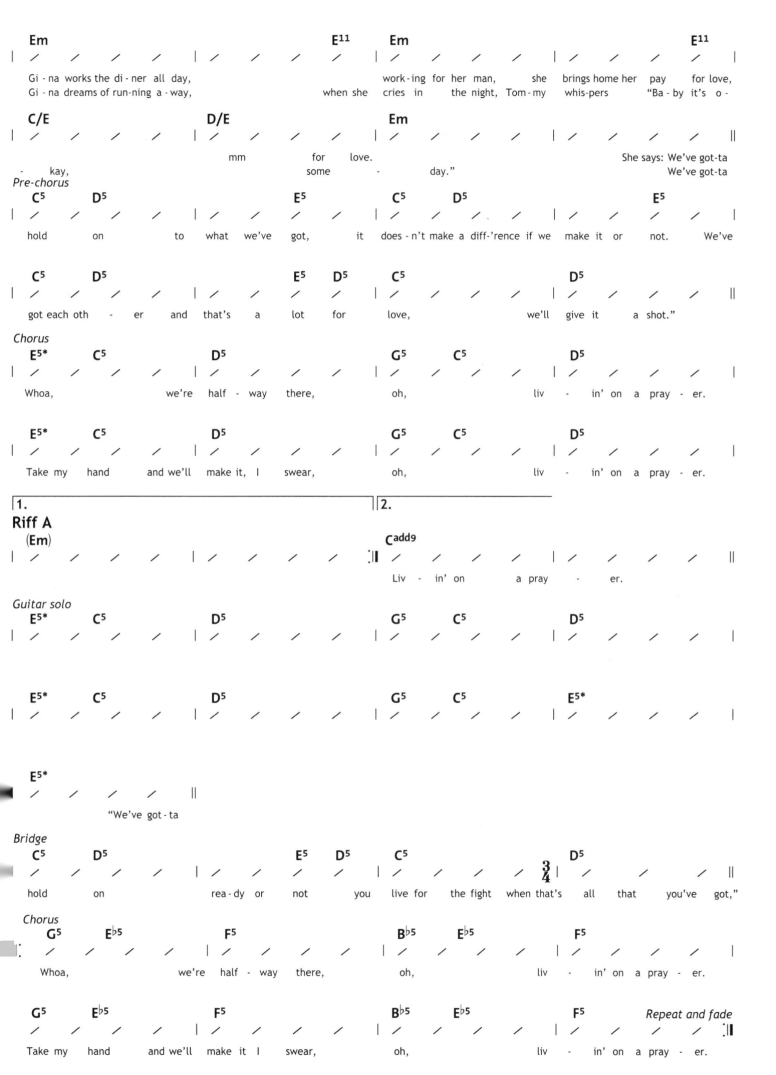

THE LOGICAL SONG

Words & Music by Roger Hodgson & Richard Davies

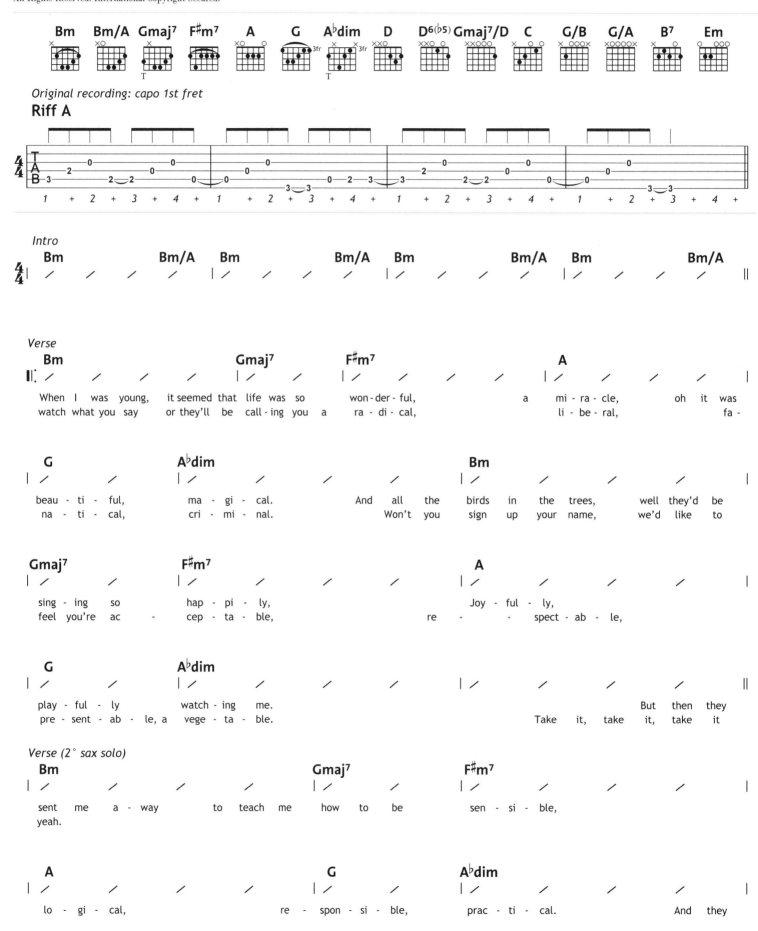

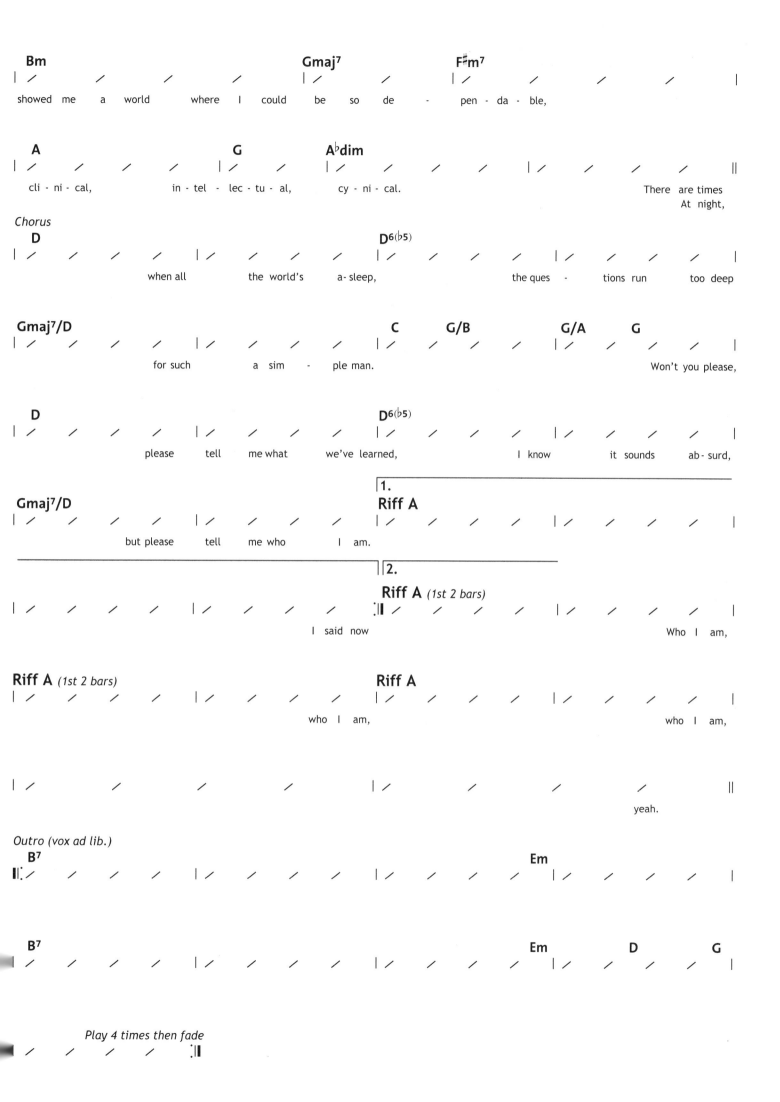

LOVE IS ALL AROUND

Words & Music by Reg Presley

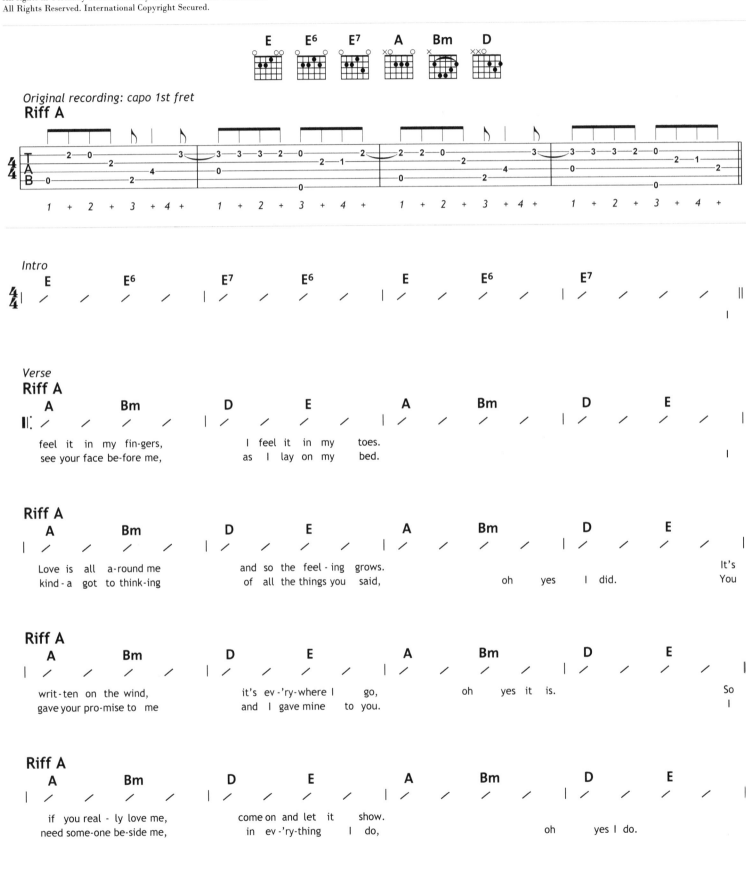

Original recording: capo 1st fret

Riff A

Intro

Verse
Riff A

feel it in my fin-gers,
see your face be-fore me,

I feel it in my toes.
as I lay on my bed.

Riff A

Love is all a-round me
kind-a got to think-ing

and so the feel-ing grows.
of all the things you said,

oh yes I did.

It's
You

Riff A

writ-ten on the wind,
gave your pro-mise to me

it's ev-'ry-where I go,
and I gave mine to you.

oh yes it is.

So
I

Riff A

if you real-ly love me,
need some-one be-side me,

come on and let it show.
in ev-'ry-thing I do,

oh yes I do.

E

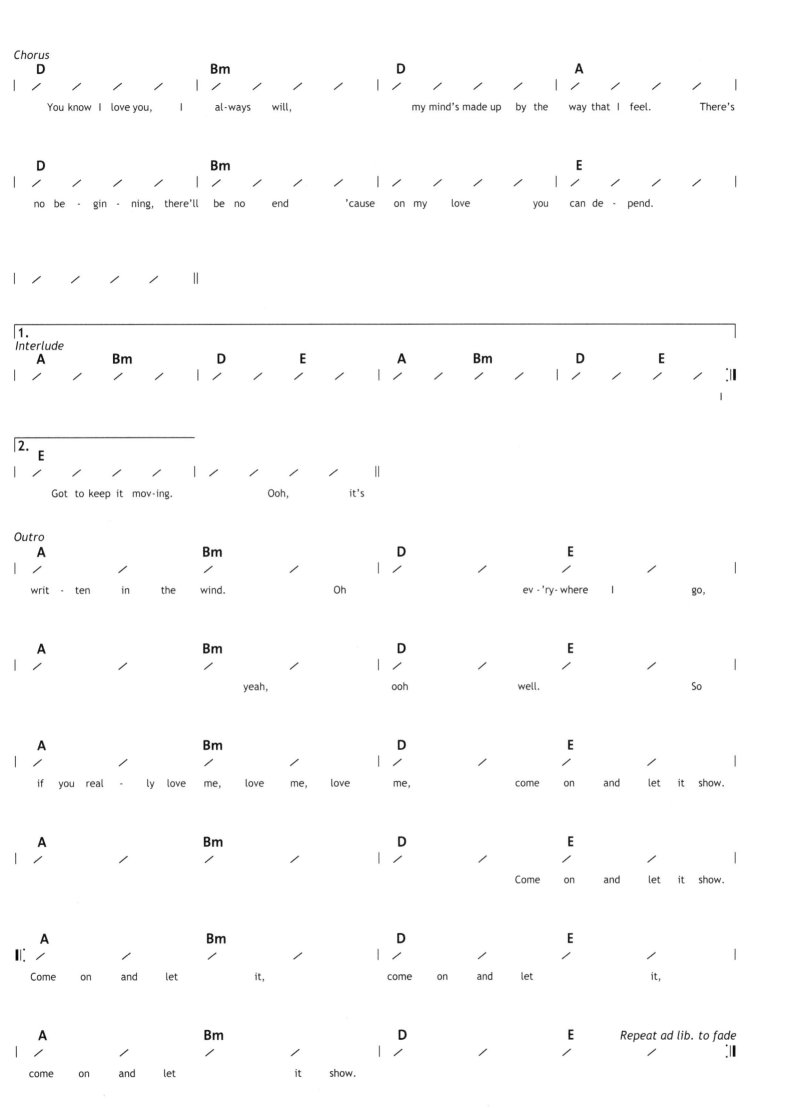

MAMMA MIA

Words & Music by Benny Andersson, Stig Anderson & Björn Ulvaeus

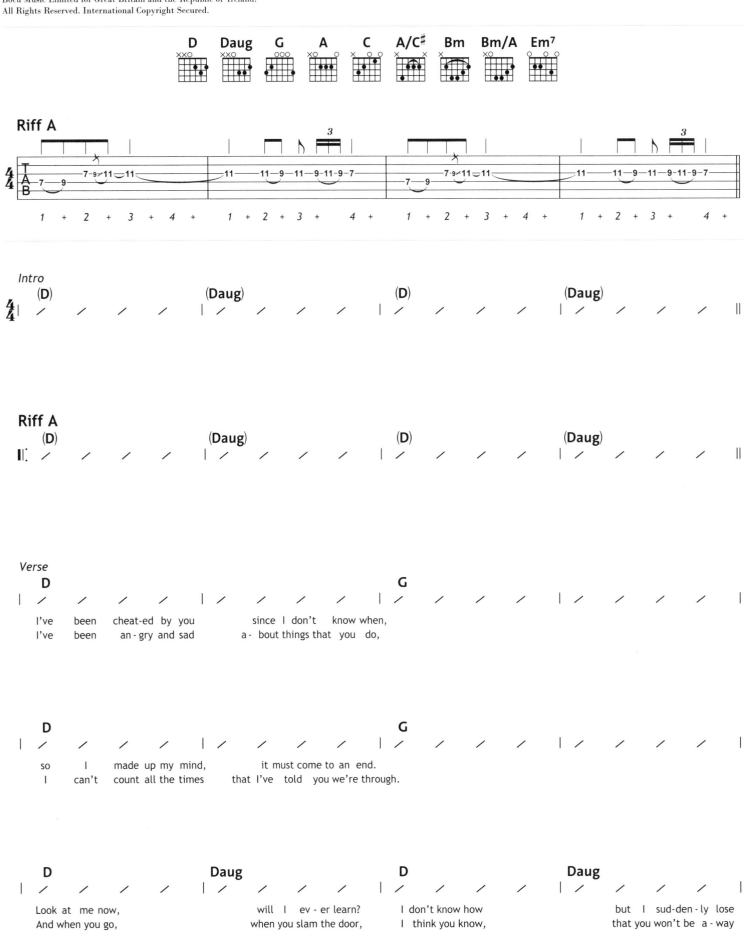

THE MAN WHO SOLD THE WORLD

Words & Music by David Bowie

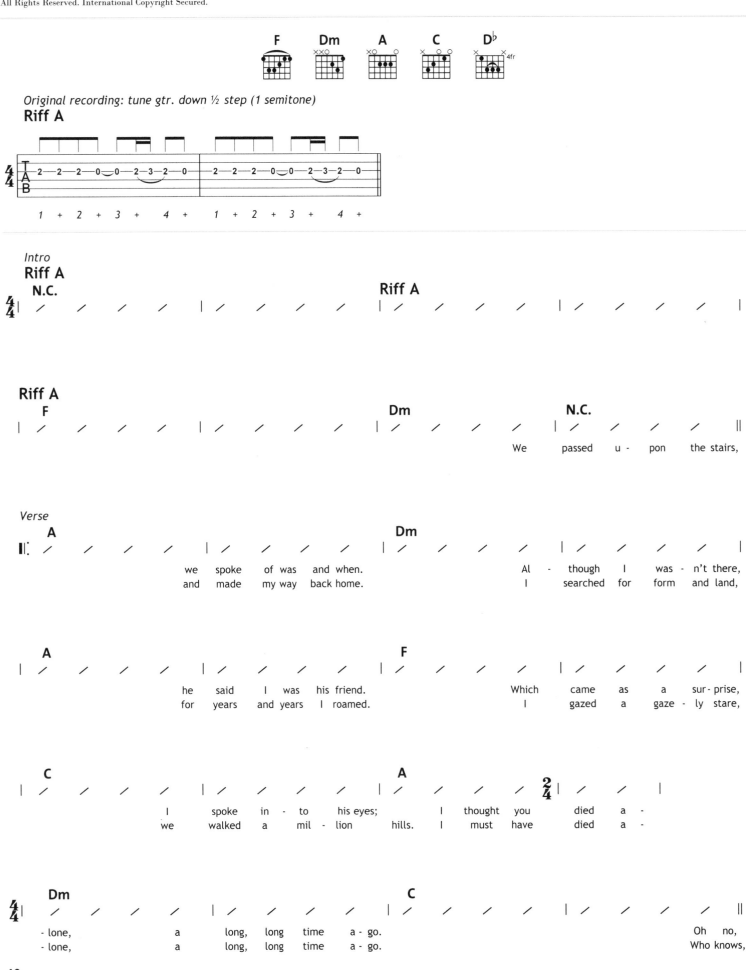

Chorus

C | / / / / | F / / / / | D♭ / / / / | F / / / / |

(𝄋) not me,   we nev-er lost con-trol,   you're face
Not me,   I   nev-er lost con-trol,   you're face,

C | / / / / | F / / / / | D♭ / / / / | *To Coda* ⊕ ‖

to face,   with the man who sold the world.

Riff A
A | / / / / | / / / / |

Riff A
Dm | / / / / |

⌐1.
/ / / / |

Riff A
F | / / / / | / / / / |

Dm | / / / / |

N.C. | / / / / :‖

I   laughed and shook his hand

⌐2.
Dm | / / / / ‖   *D.S. al Coda*

Who knows?

⊕ *Coda*

Riff A
A | / / / / | / / / / |

Riff A
Dm | / / / / | / / / / ‖

Riff A
F ‖: / / / / | / / / / |

Riff A
Dm | / / / / | / / / / |

Riff A
A | / / / / | / / / / |

Riff A
Dm | / / / / | / / / / :‖   *Play 3 times*

F | / / / / ‖

MESSAGE IN A BOTTLE

Words & Music by Sting

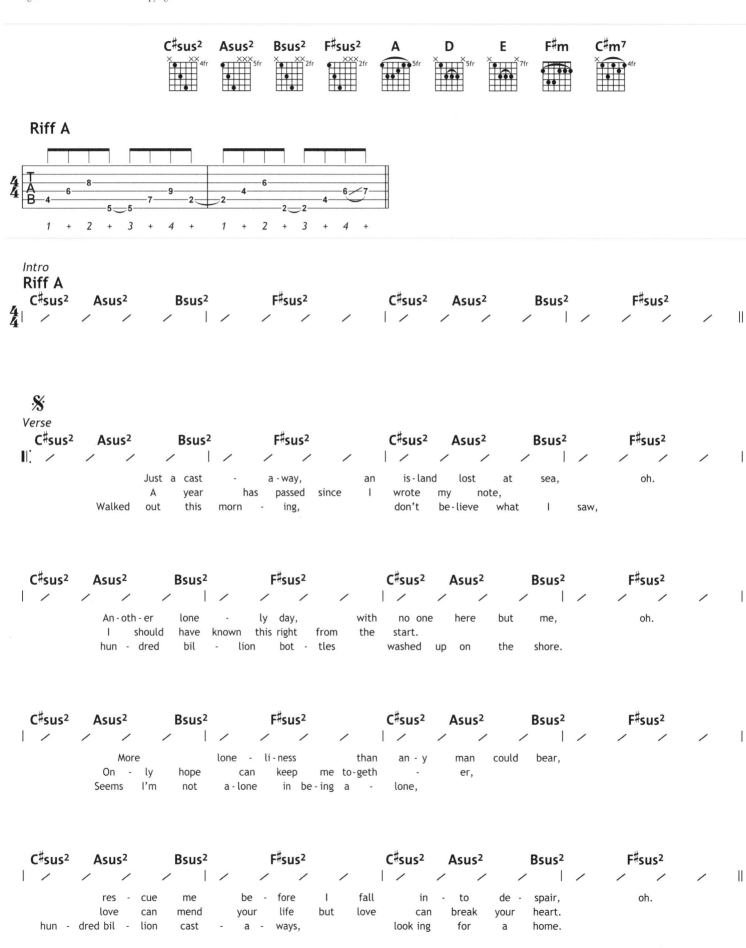

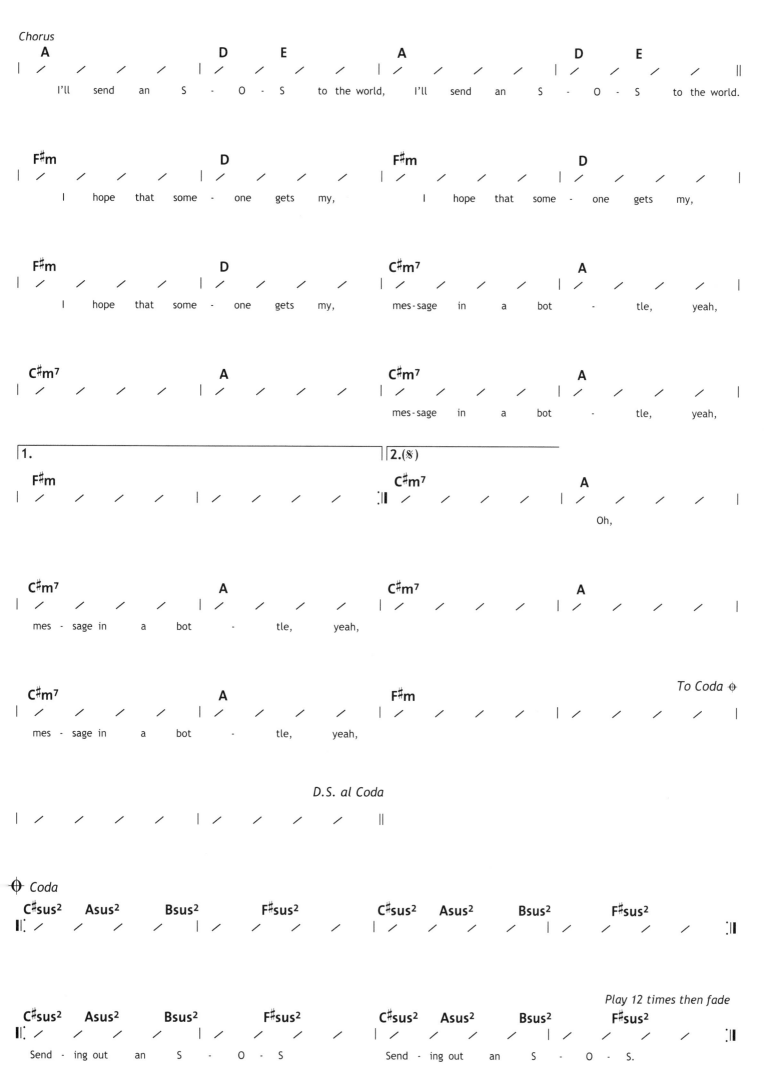

MRS. ROBINSON

Words & Music by Paul Simon

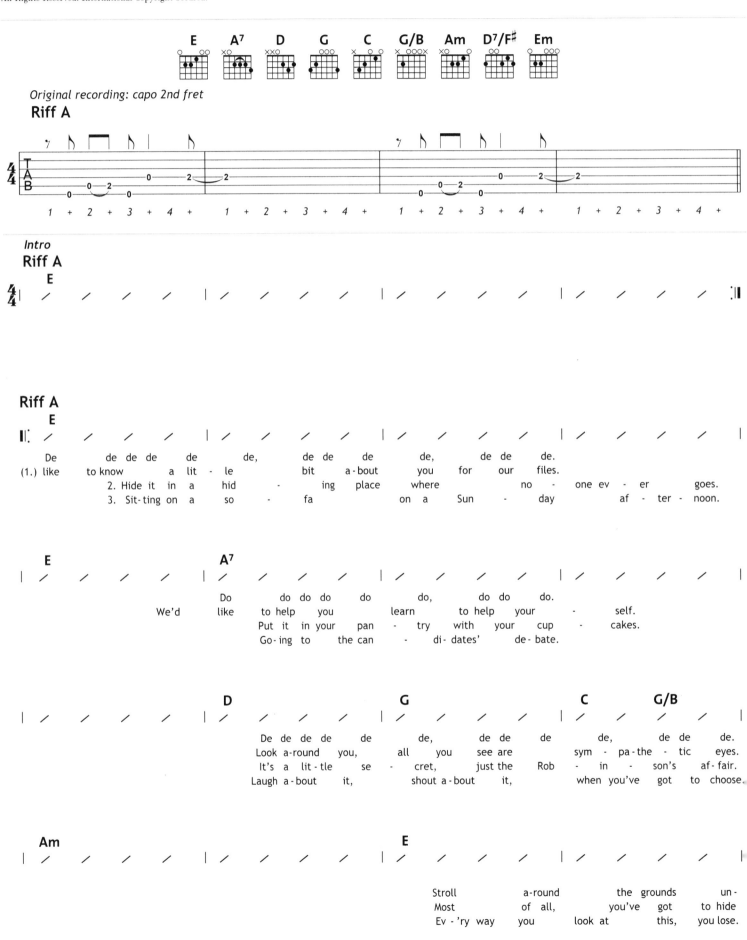

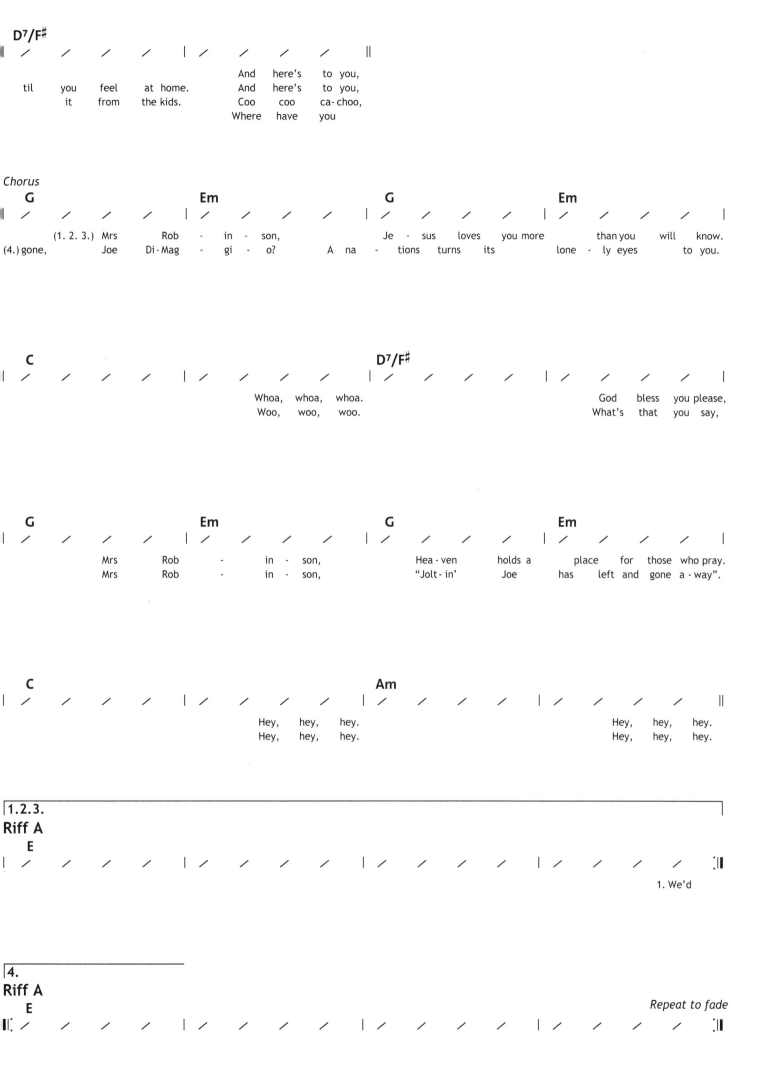

NINE TO FIVE

Words & Music by Dolly Parton

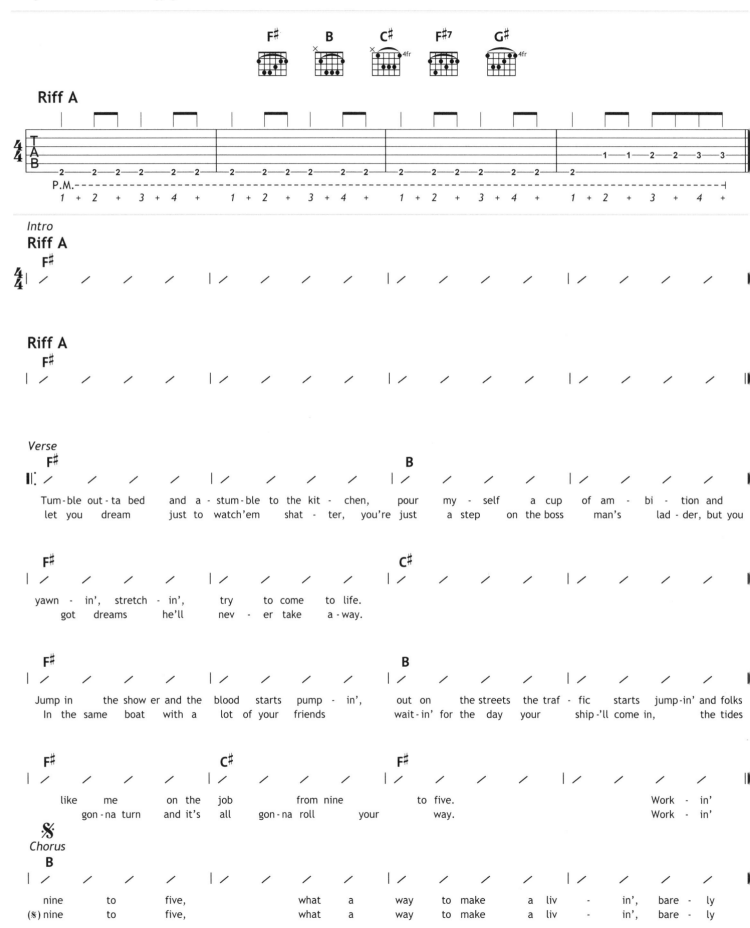

F#7

get - tin' by,   it's all   ta - kin', and   no   giv   -   in'. They   just
get - tin' by,   it's all   ta - kin', and   no   giv   -   in'. They   just

B

use   your   mind,   then   they   nev - er give   you   cre - dit,   it's   e -
use   your   mind,   and   you   nev - er get   the   cre - dit,   it's   e -

G#   **C#**

- nough   to   drive   you   cra - zy if   you   let   it.
- nough   to   drive   you   cra - zy if   you   let   it.

B

Nine   to   five,   for   ser - vice and   de - vo - tion, you   would
Nine   to   five,   yeah,   they   got   you where   they want   you,   there's   a

F#7

think   that   I   would   de - serve   a   fair   pro - mo - tion. Want   to
bet - ter   life   and   you   think   a - bout   it   don't   you.   It's   a

                                             To Coda ⊕

B

move   a - head,   but   the   boss   won't   seem   to   let   me,   I
rich   man's   game,   no   mat - ter   what   they   call   it,   and   you

                                                         1.

G#   **C#**

swear   some - times   that   man   is   out   to   get   me.
spend   your   life   put - tin'   mon - ey   in   his   wal -

Riff A

F#

Mmm   They

2.

C#   *D.S. al Coda*

- - let

⊕ *Coda*

B   **G#**   **C#**

it,   and   you   spend   your   life   put - tin'   mon - ey   in   his   wal -

Fade out

- let.

NORWEGIAN WOOD (THIS BIRD HAS FLOWN)

Words & Music by John Lennon & Paul McCartney

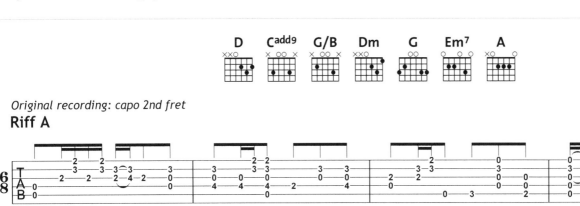

Original recording: capo 2nd fret

Riff A

Riff A

(D)   (Cadd⁹) (G/B) (D)

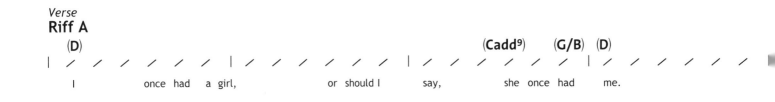

Verse
Riff A

(D)   (Cadd⁹) (G/B) (D)

I   once had a girl,   or should I   say,   she once had   me.

Riff A

(D)   (Cadd⁹) (G/B) (D)

She   showed me her   room,   is - n't it   good,   Nor - we - gian   Wood?   She

Bridge
Dm   **G**

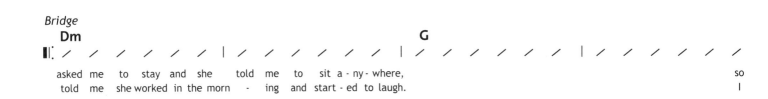

asked me   to stay and she   told me to sit a - ny - where,   so
told me   she worked in the morn   -   ing and start - ed to laugh.   I

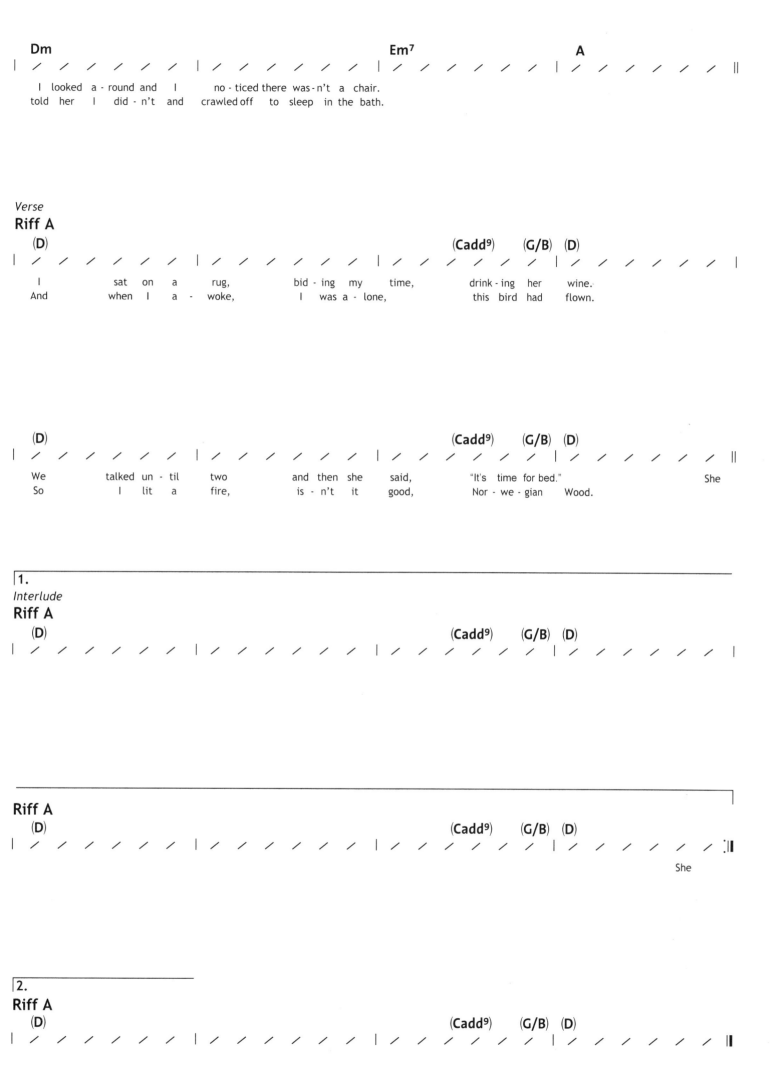

Dm

I looked a-round and I no-ticed there was-n't a chair.
told her I did-n't and crawled off to sleep in the bath.

Em⁷

A

Verse
Riff A
(D)

I sat on a rug, bid-ing my time, drink-ing her wine.
And when I a-woke, I was a-lone, this bird had flown.

(Cadd⁹) **(G/B)** **(D)**

(D)

We talked un-til two and then she said, "It's time for bed." She
So I lit a fire, is-n't it good, Nor-we-gian Wood.

(Cadd⁹) **(G/B)** **(D)**

1.
Interlude
Riff A
(D)

(Cadd⁹) **(G/B)** **(D)**

Riff A
(D)

(Cadd⁹) **(G/B)** **(D)**

She

2.
Riff A
(D)

(Cadd⁹) **(G/B)** **(D)**

NOTHING ELSE MATTERS

Words & Music by James Hetfield & Lars Ulrich

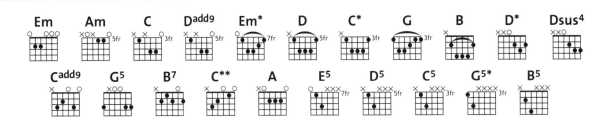

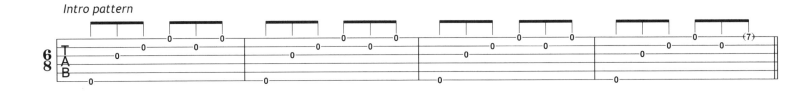

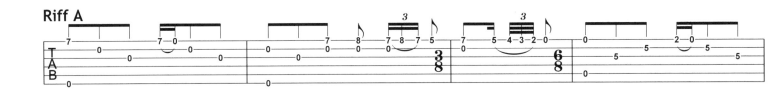

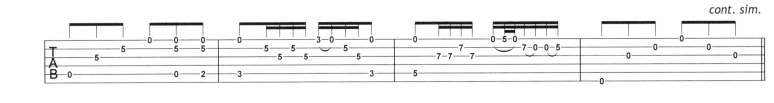

| | / / / / / | / / / / / | / / / / / ‖ |

‖: **Em*** / / / / / | **D** **C** / / / / / | [1] **Em*** / / / / / | **D** **C** / / / / / :‖

[2.] **G** **B** **Em**
| / / / / / | / / / / / | / / / / / ‖

𝄋

Verse

‖: **Em** / / / / / / | **D*** **Dsus⁴** / **C**add9 / / / |

(1.4.) So close no mat - ter how far,
(2.5.) Nev - er o - pened my self this way,
(3.6.) Trust I seek and I find in you,

Em / / / / / / | **D*** **Dsus⁴** / **C**add9 / / / |

could - n't be much more from the heart.
life is ours, we live it our way.
ev - 'ry day for us some - thing new.

Em / / / / / / | **D*** **Dsus⁴** / **C**add9 / / / |

For - ev - er trust - ing who we are,
All these words I don't just say,
O - pen mind for a diff - 'rent view,

6° *To Coda* ⊕

G⁵ / / / / / / | **Em** / / / / / |

and no - thing else mat - ters.
and no - thing else mat - ters.
and no - thing else mat - ters.

B⁷

[1.2.5.] / / / / / / :‖ [3.4.] **C*** / / / **A** / / ‖

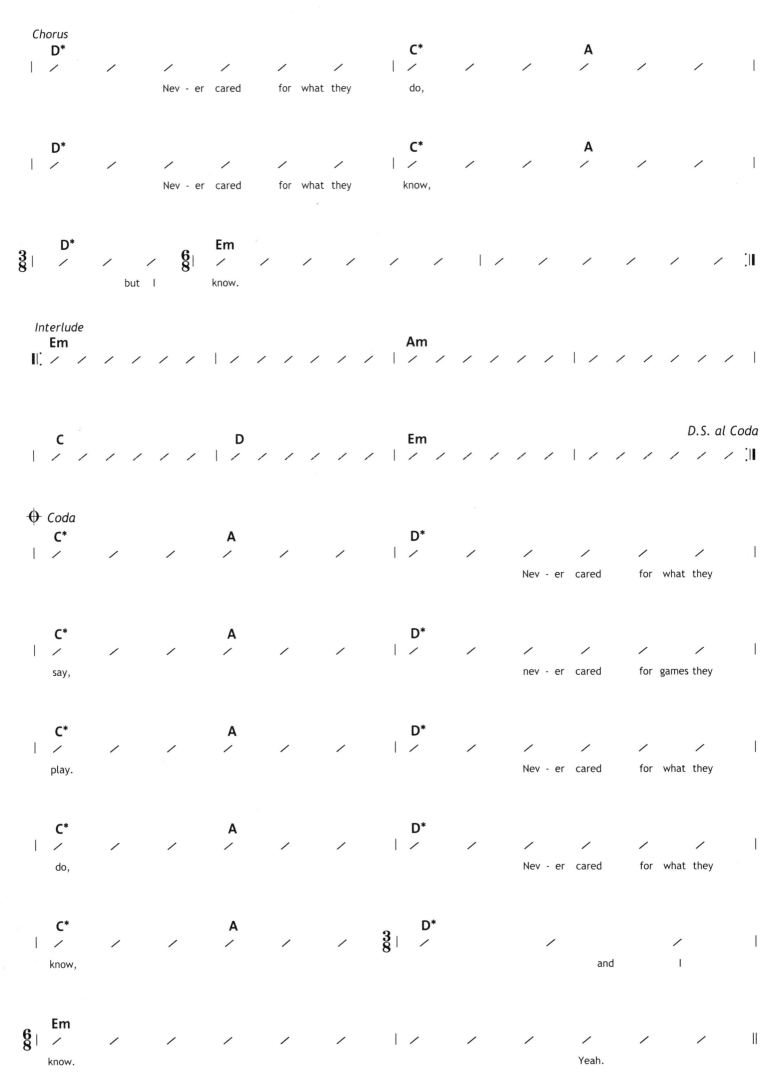

54

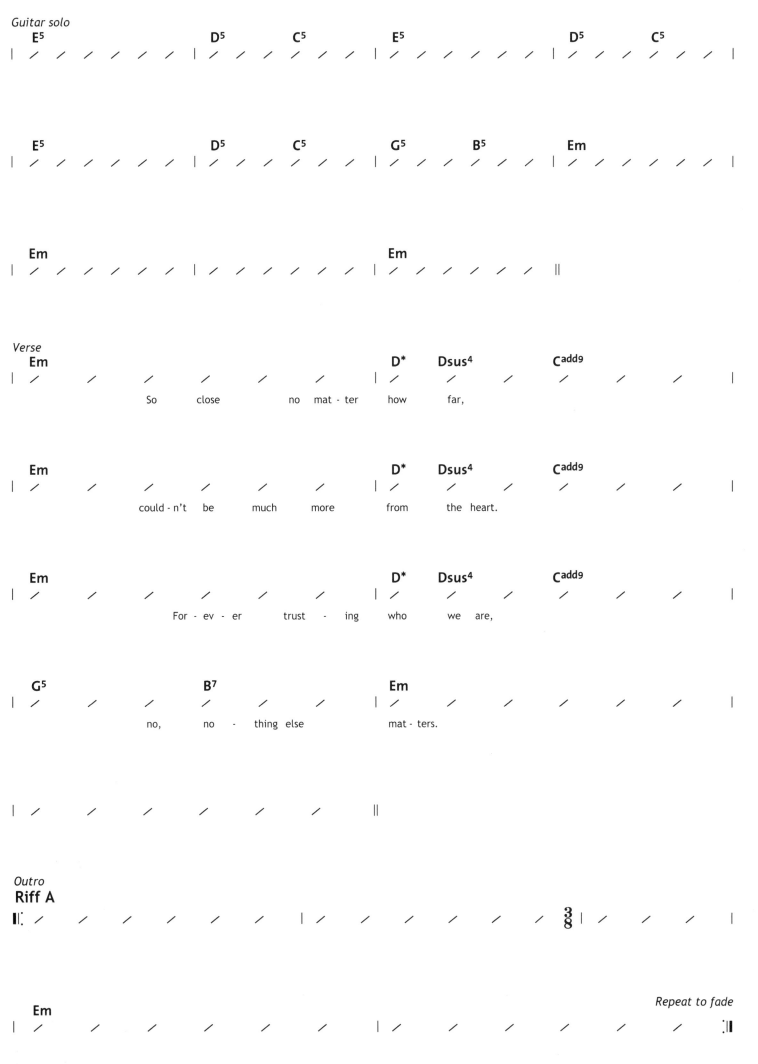

LAYLA

Words & Music by Eric Clapton & Jim Gordon

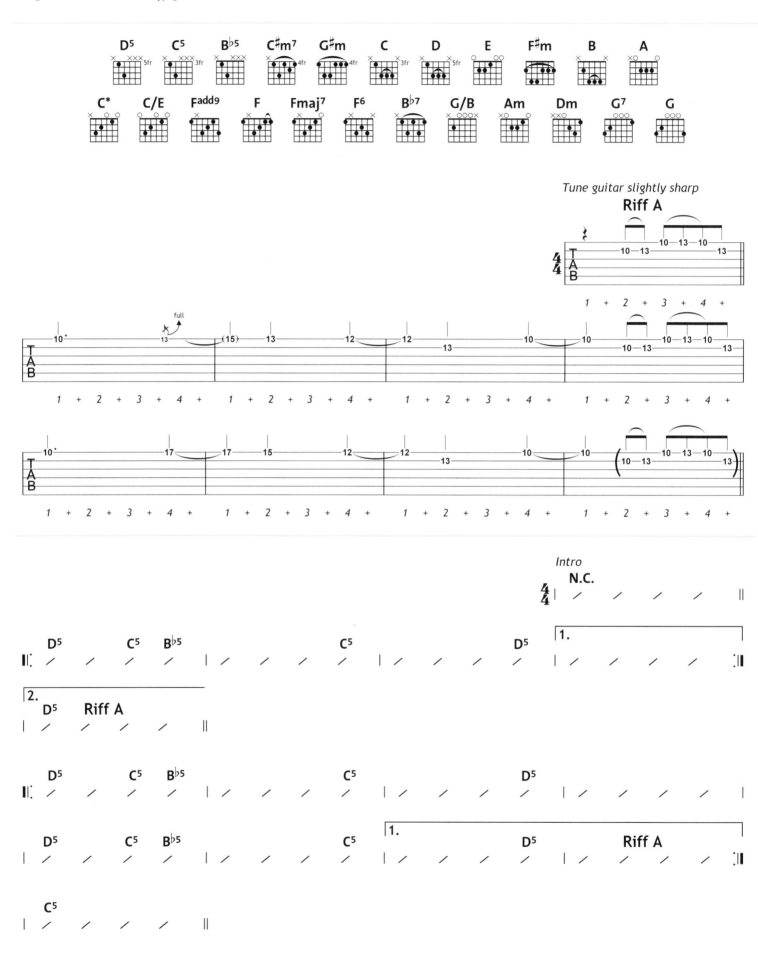

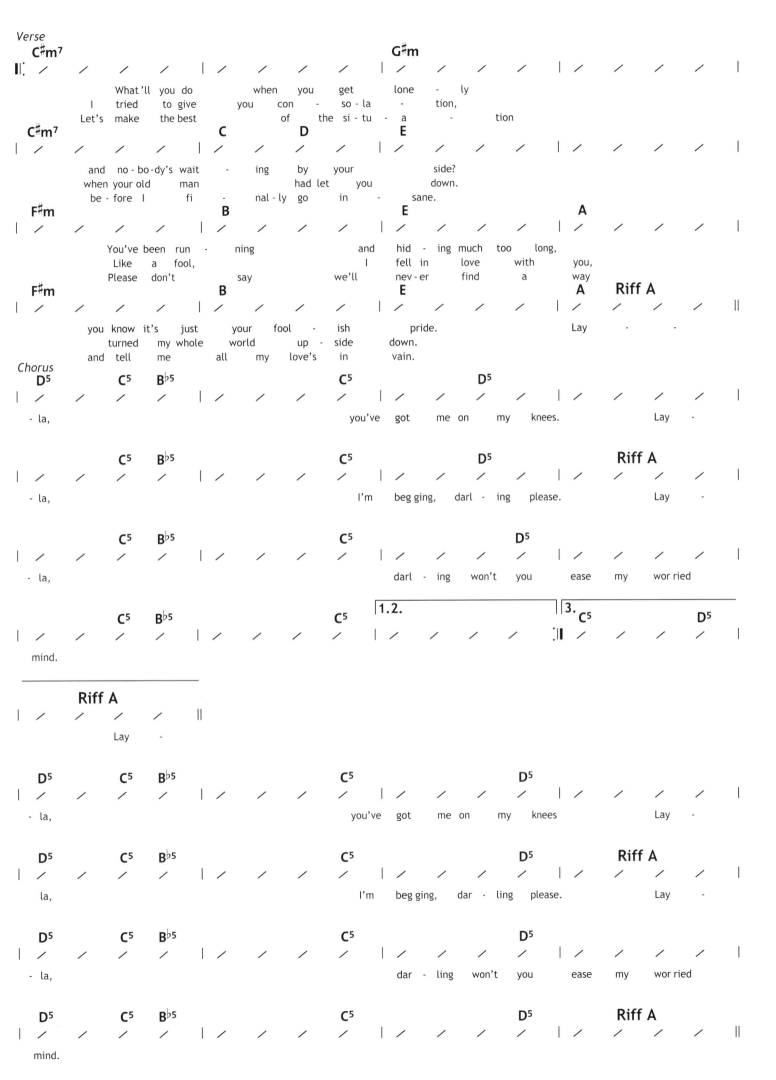

Solo

| D5 | | C5 | B♭5 | | | | | C5 | | | | D5 | | | | |

| D5 | | C5 | B♭5 | | | | | C5 | **1-5.** | | | D5 | | | | |

6. C5

Outro (half time feel)

| C* | | | | C/E | | | | Fadd9 | F | Fmaj7 | | F6 | | F | |

| C* | | | | C/E | | | | Fadd9 | F | Fmaj7 | | F6 | | F | |

| B♭7 | | | | | | | | C* | | | | | | | |

| C* | | | | C/E | | | | Fadd9 | F | Fmaj7 | | F6 | | F | |

| B♭7 | | | | | | | | C* | | | | | | | |

| C* | | | | C/E | | | | Fadd9 | F | Fmaj7 | | F6 | | F | |

| B♭7 | | | | | | | | C* | | | | | | | G/B |

| Am | | | | Dm | | | | G7 | | | | C | | G/B | |

| Am | | | | Dm | | | | G | | | | | | | |

| C* | | | | C/E | | | | Fadd9 | F | Fmaj7 | | F6 | | F | |

| B♭7 | | | | | | | | C* | | | | | | | |

Play 5 times

| C* | | | | C/E | | | | Fadd9 | F | Fmaj7 | | F6 | | F | |

| B♭7 | | | | | | | | C | | | | | |

ORDINARY WORLD

Words & Music by John Taylor, Nick Rhodes, Simon Le Bon & Warren Cuccurullo

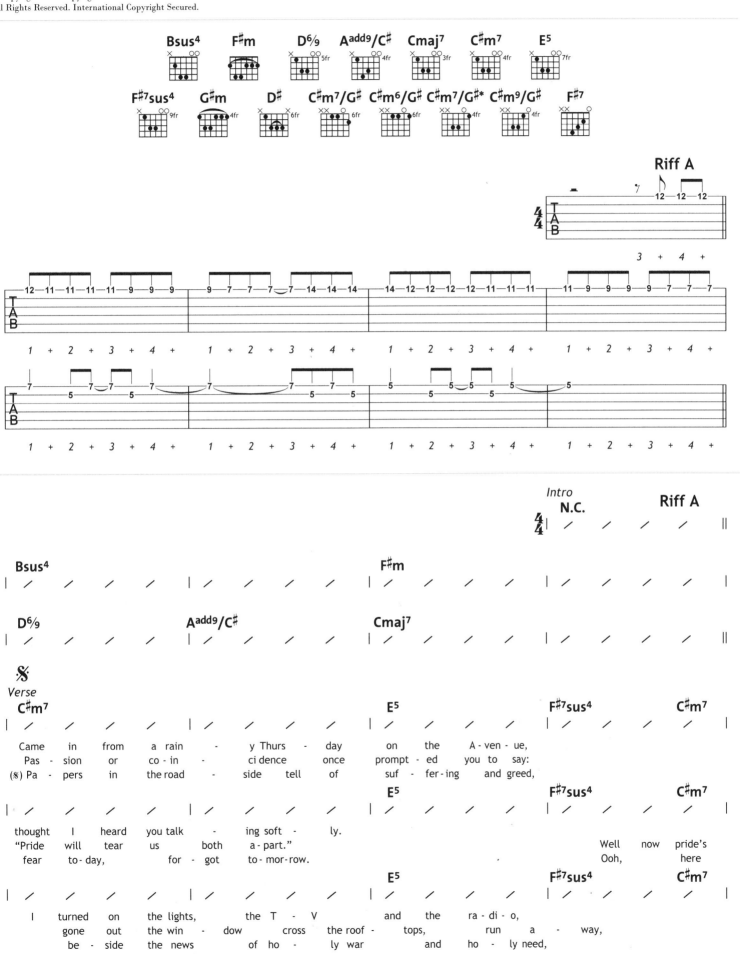

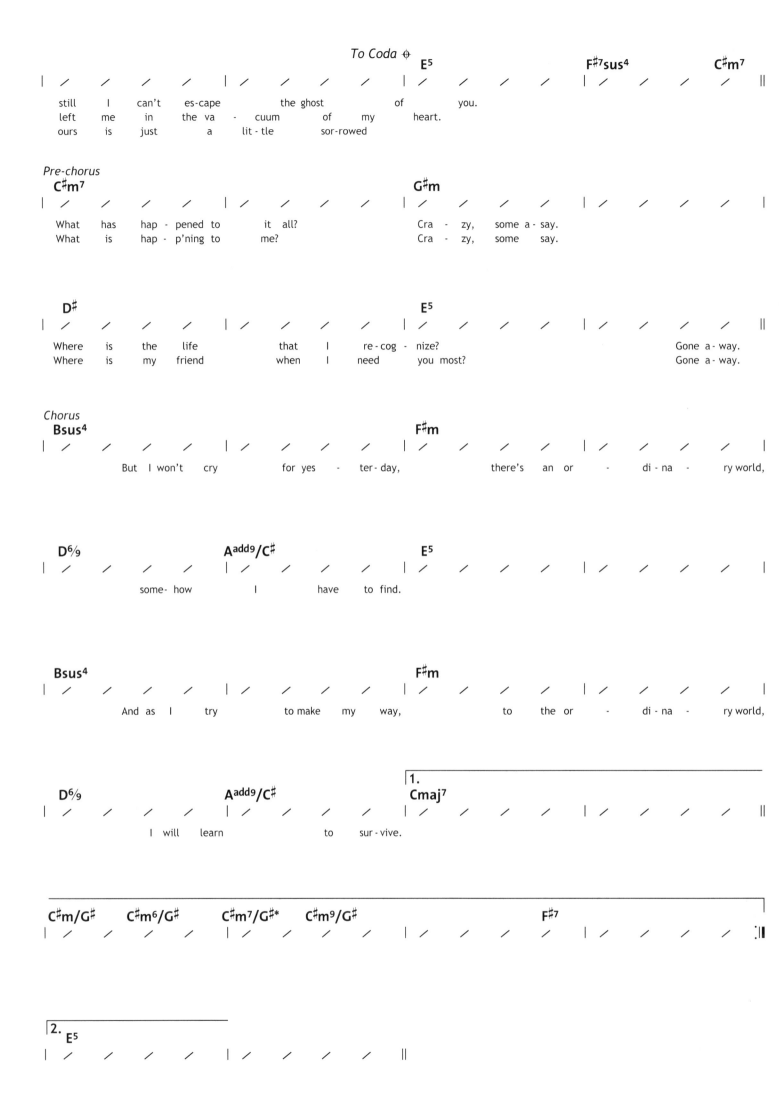

To Coda ⊕ **E5** **F♯7sus4** **C♯m7**

still   I   can't   es-cape   the ghost   of   you.
left   me   in   the va - cuum   of   my   heart.
ours   is   just   a   lit - tle   sor-rowed

Pre-chorus
C♯m7 **G♯m**

What   has   hap - pened to   it all?   Cra - zy,   some a - say.
What   is   hap - p'ning to   me?   Cra - zy,   some   say.

D♯ **E5**

Where   is   the   life   that   I   re - cog - nize?   Gone a - way.
Where   is   my   friend   when   I   need   you most?   Gone a - way.

Chorus
Bsus4 **F♯m**

But I   won't   cry   for yes - ter- day,   there's   an   or - di - na - ry world,

D6/9 **Aadd9/C♯** **E5**

some- how   I   have   to find.

Bsus4 **F♯m**

And as   I   try   to make   my   way,   to   the   or - di - na - ry world,

D6/9 **Aadd9/C♯** **1.** **Cmaj7**

I will   learn   to   sur - vive.

C♯m/G♯   **C♯m6/G♯**   **C♯m7/G♯***   **C♯m9/G♯**   **F♯7**

2. **E5**

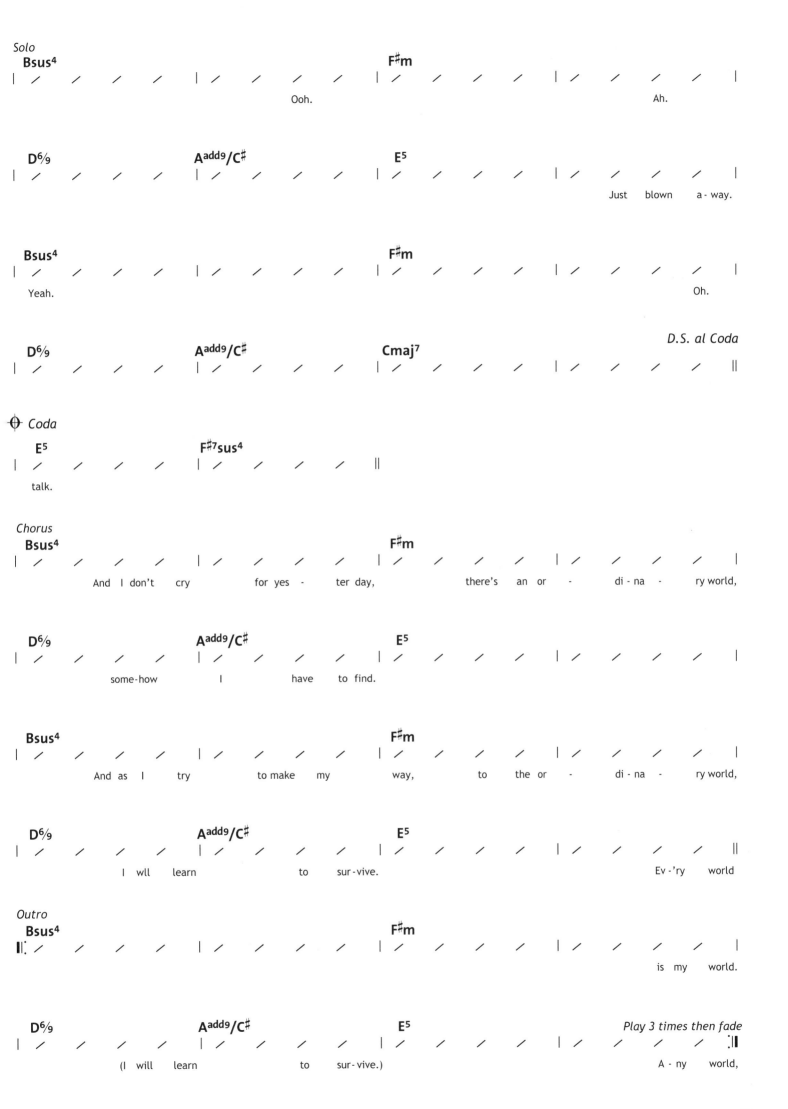

Solo
Bsus⁴ / / / / | / / / / **F♯m** / / / / | / / / / |
Ooh.   Ah.

D⁶⁄₉ / / / / | **Aadd9/C♯** / / / / | **E⁵** / / / / | / / / / |
Just blown a - way.

Bsus⁴ / / / / | / / / / **F♯m** / / / / | / / / / |
Yeah.   Oh.

D.S. al Coda

D⁶⁄₉ / / / / | **Aadd9/C♯** / / / / | **Cmaj⁷** / / / / | / / / / ‖

✛ *Coda*
E⁵ / / / / | **F♯⁷sus⁴** / / / / ‖
talk.

Chorus
Bsus⁴ / / / / | / / / / **F♯m** / / / | / / / |
And I don't cry   for yes - ter day,   there's an or - di - na - ry world,

D⁶⁄₉ / / / / | **Aadd9/C♯** / / / / | **E⁵** / / / | / / / |
some-how   I   have to find.

Bsus⁴ / / / / | / / / / **F♯m** / / / | / / / |
And as I   try   to make my   way,   to the or - di - na - ry world,

D⁶⁄₉ / / / / | **Aadd9/C♯** / / / / | **E⁵** / / / | / / / ‖
I will learn   to sur - vive.   Ev - 'ry world

Outro
Bsus⁴ ‖: / / / / | / / / / **F♯m** / / / | / / / |
is my world.

D⁶⁄₉ / / / / | **Aadd9/C♯** / / / / | **E⁵** / / / | *Play 3 times then fade* / / / :‖
(I will learn   to sur - vive.)   A - ny world,

PAPERBACK WRITER

Words & Music by John Lennon & Paul McCartney

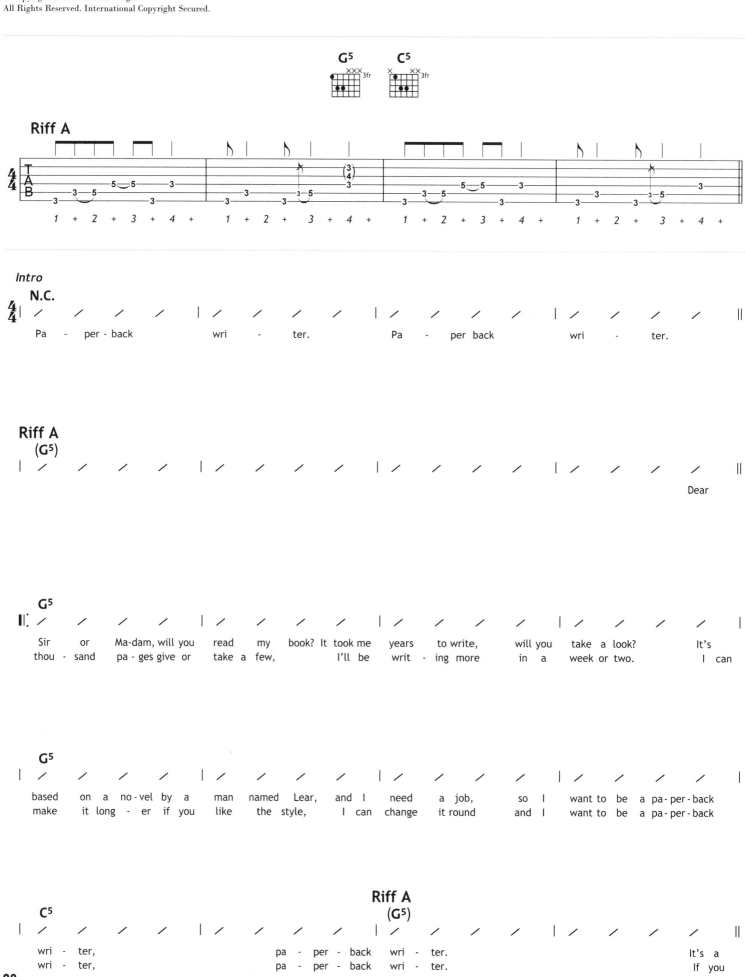

Verse

G⁵

| / / / / | / / / / | / / / / | / / / / |

dir - ty sto - ry of a dir - ty man, and his cling - ing wife does-n't un - der - stand. His

real - ly like it you can have the rights, it could make a mil - lion for you ov - er night. If you

G⁵

| / / / / | / / / / | / / / / | / / / / |

son is work - ing for the Dai - ly Mail, it's a stea - dy job but he wants to be a pa - per- back

must re - turn it, you can send it here, but I need a break and I want to be a pa - per- back

C⁵   **G⁵**

| / / / / | / / / / | / / / / | / / / / ||

wri - ter,   pa - per - back wri - ter.

wri - ter,   pa - per - back wri - ter.

Chorus

N.C.

| / / / / | / / / / | / / / / | / / / / |

Pa - per - back wri - ter. Pa - per - back wri - ter.

1.

Riff A

(G⁵)

| / / / / | / / / / | / / / / | / / / / :||

It's a

2.

Riff A

(G⁵)

| / / / / | / / / / | / / / / | / / / / ||

Outro

                                                 Repeat to fade

G⁵

||: / / / / | / / / / | / / / / | / / / / :||

Pa - per - back wri - ter. (Pa - per - back wri - ter.)

PURPLE RAIN

Words & Music by Prince

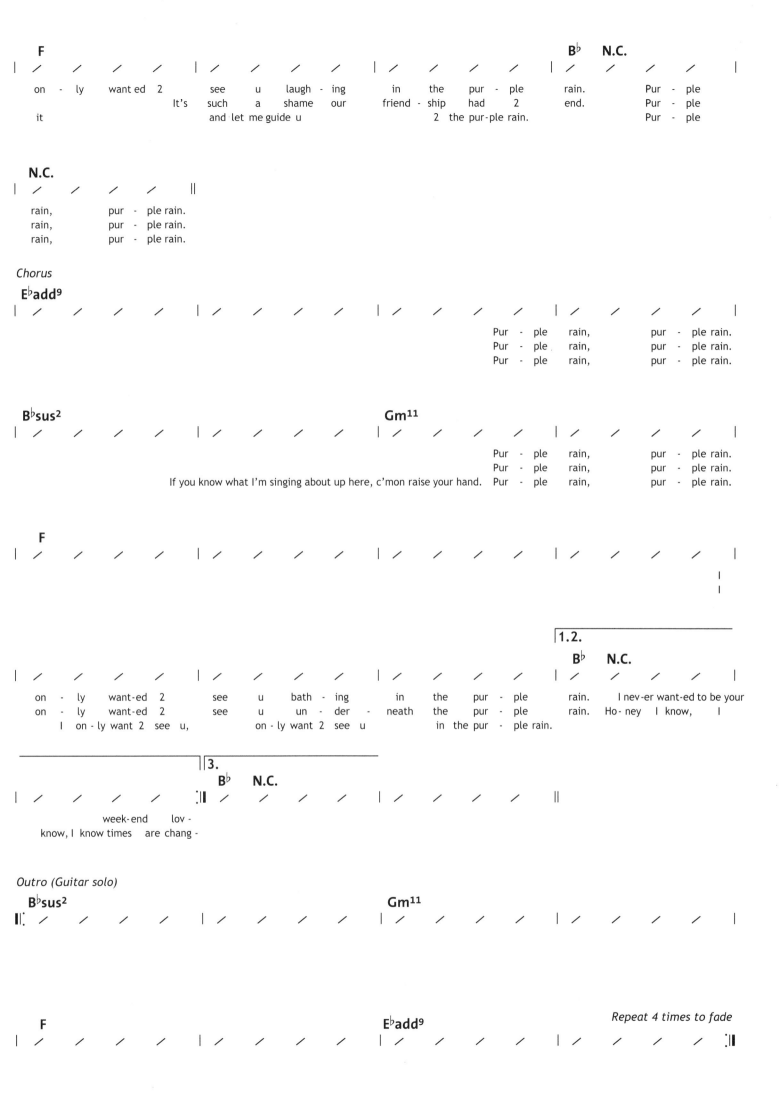

F   Bᵇ N.C.

on - ly want ed 2   see u laugh - ing   in the pur - ple rain.   Pur - ple
It's such a shame our   friend - ship had 2 end.   Pur - ple
it   and let me guide u   2 the pur-ple rain.   Pur - ple

N.C.

rain,   pur - ple rain.
rain,   pur - ple rain.
rain,   pur - ple rain.

Chorus

Eᵇadd⁹

                                     Pur - ple rain,   pur - ple rain.
                                       Pur - ple rain,   pur - ple rain.
                                       Pur - ple rain,   pur - ple rain.

Bᵇsus²   Gm¹¹

                                     Pur - ple rain,   pur - ple rain.
                                     Pur - ple rain,   pur - ple rain.
If you know what I'm singing about up here, c'mon raise your hand. Pur - ple rain,   pur - ple rain.

F

on - ly want-ed 2   see u bath - ing   in the pur - ple

1.2.

Bᵇ N.C.

on - ly want-ed 2   see u bath - ing   in the pur - ple rain.   I nev-er want-ed to be your
on - ly want-ed 2   see u un - der - neath the pur - ple rain.   Ho - ney I know,   I
I on - ly want 2 see u,   on - ly want 2 see u   in the pur - ple rain.

3.

Bᵇ N.C.

week-end lov -
know, I know times are chang -

Outro (Guitar solo)

Bᵇsus²   Gm¹¹

F   Eᵇadd⁹   *Repeat 4 times to fade*

ROSANNA

Words & Music by David Paich

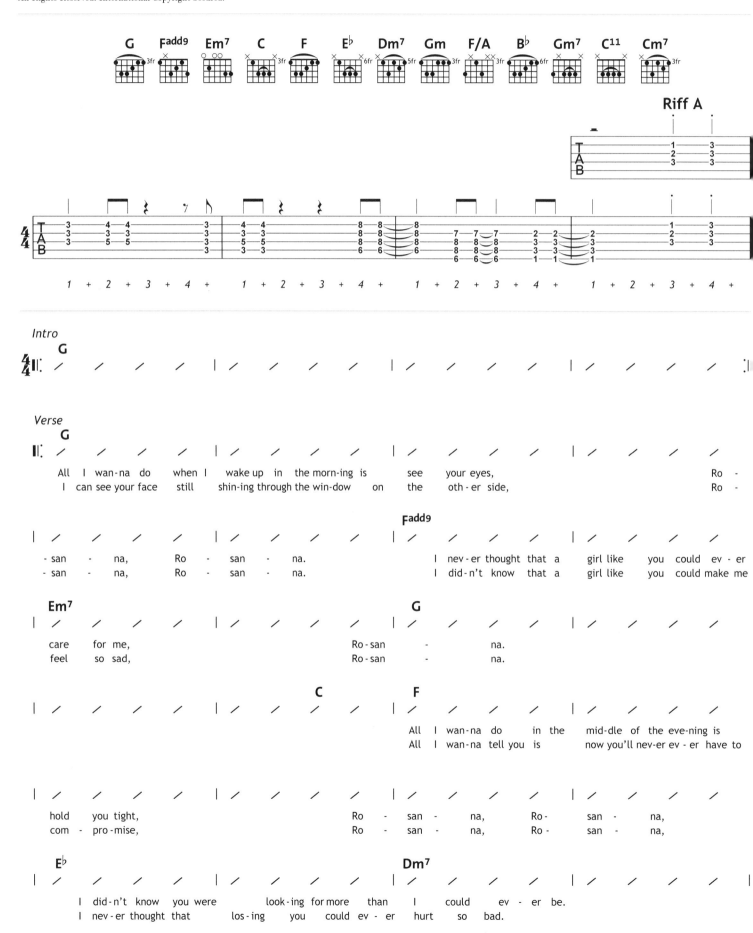

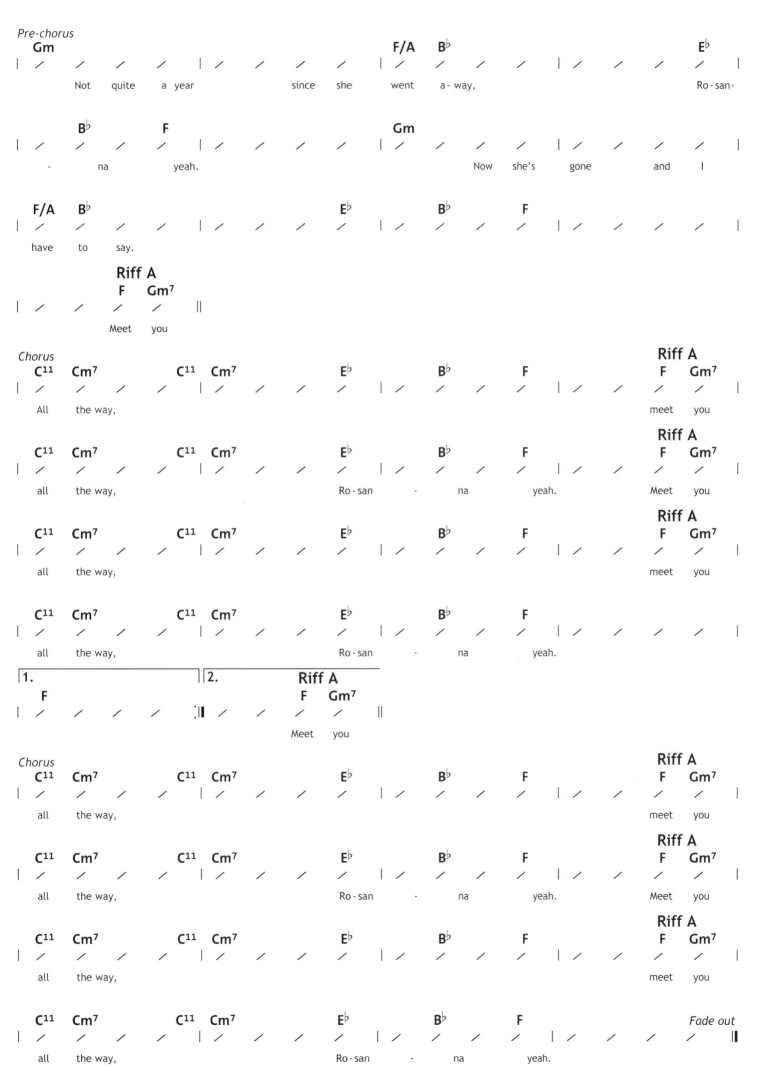

SHOULD I STAY OR SHOULD I GO

Words & Music by Joe Strummer & Mick Jones

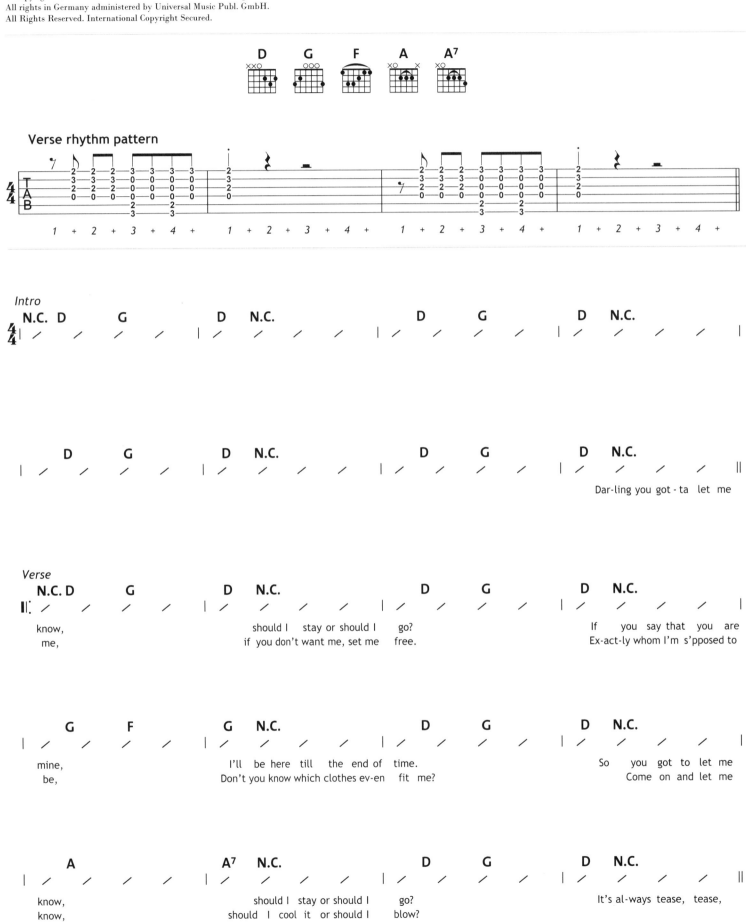

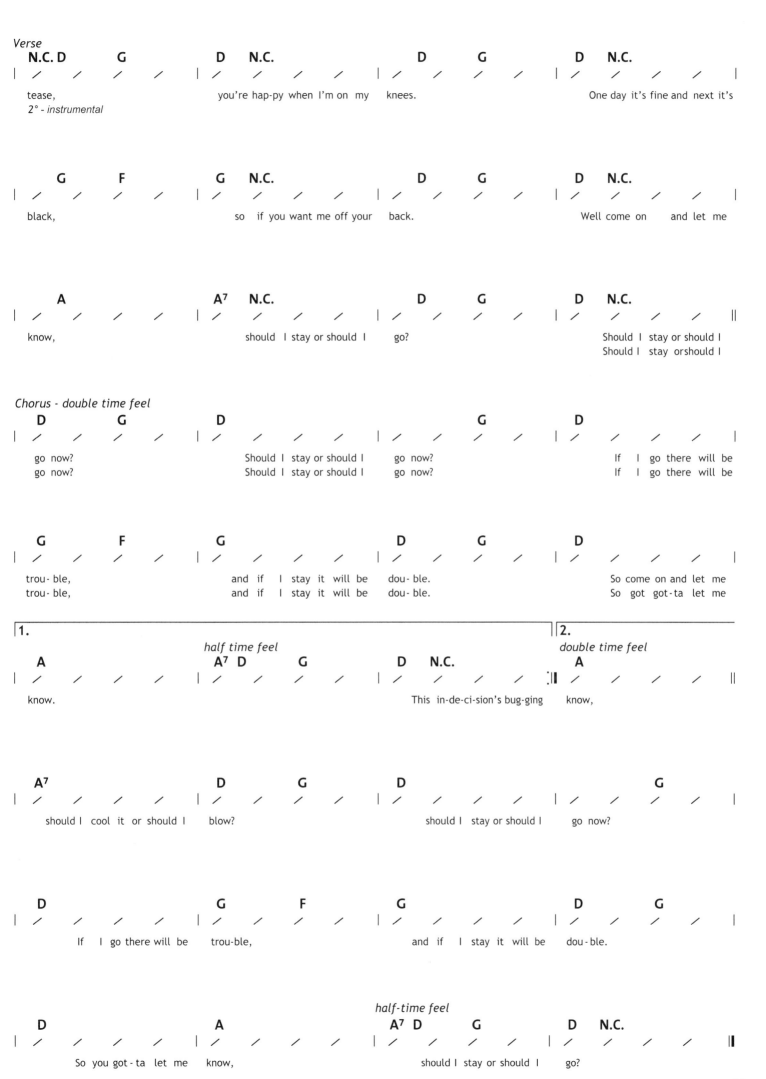

(SITTIN' ON) THE DOCK OF THE BAY

Words & Music by Steve Cropper & Otis Redding

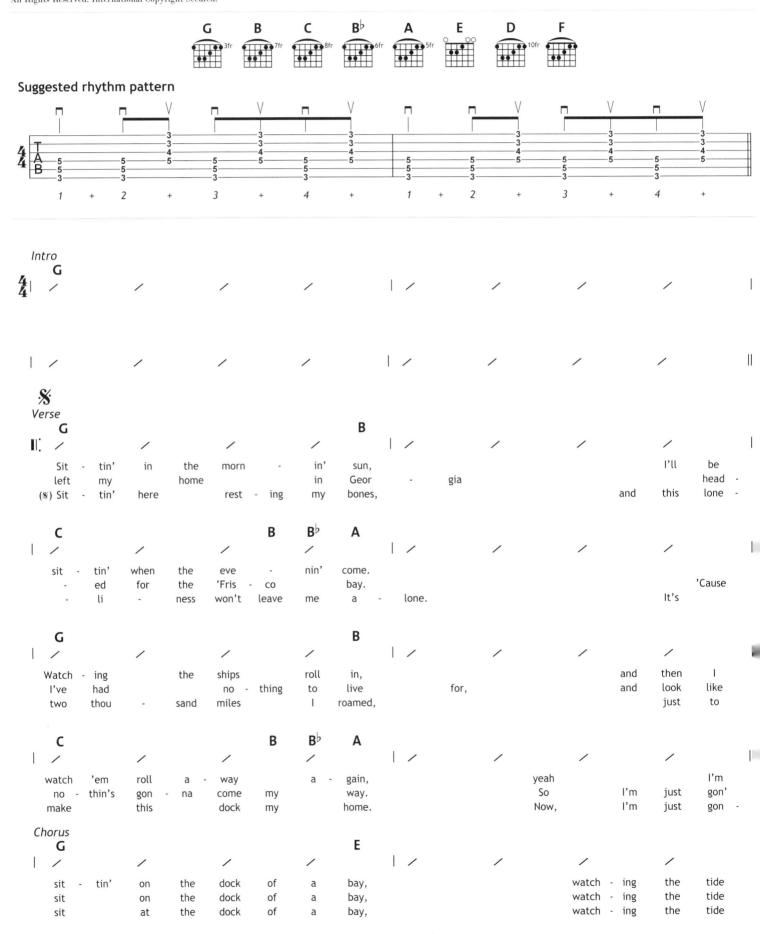

G / / / / **E** | / / / / |

roll a - way.   Ooh,   I'm   just
roll a - way.   Ooh,   I'm
roll a - way.   Ooh - ee,   I'm

G / / / / **A** | / / / / |

sit - tin' on the dock of a bay,   wast - in' time.
sit - tin' on the dock of a bay,   wast - in' time.
sit - tin' on the dock of a bay,   wast - in' time.

To Coda ✛

G / / / / **E** | / / / / :||

Bridge

G / / **D** / **C** | / / / / |

Look like no - thing's gon - na change,

G / / **D** / **C** | / / / / ||

Ev - 'ry - thing still re - mains the same.

G / / **D** / **C** / **G** / | / / / / |

I can't do what ten peo - ple tell me to do,

F / / / / **D** | / / / / ||

D.S. al Coda

so I guess I'll re - main the same, yes.

✛ *Coda*

E / / / / ||

G ||: / / / / | / / / / |

(whistle)

Repeat and fade

E / / / / | / / / / :||

71

SOUL MAN

Words & Music by Isaac Hayes & David Porter

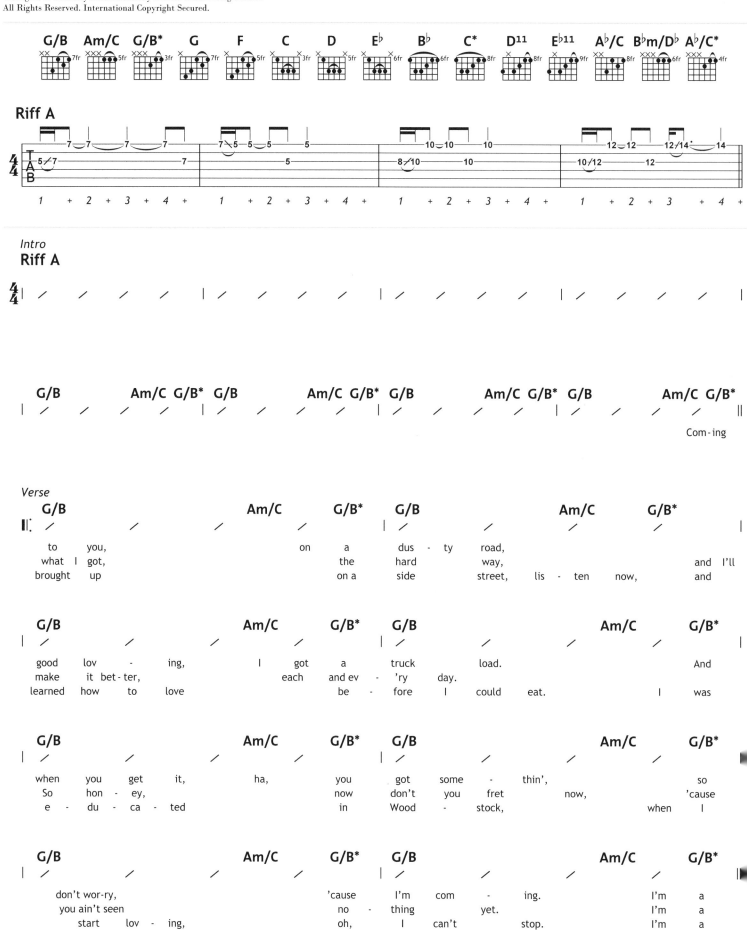

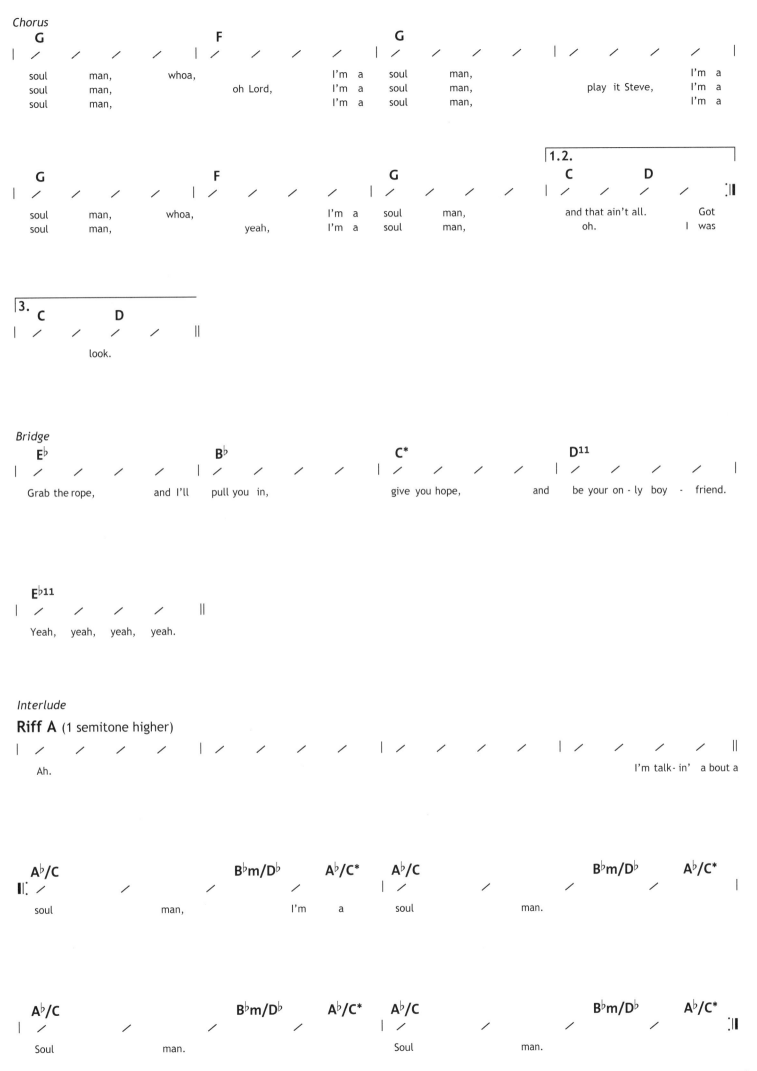

73

PINBALL WIZARD

Words & Music by Pete Townshend

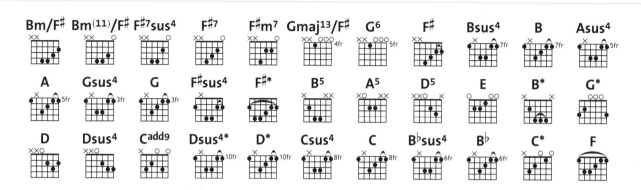

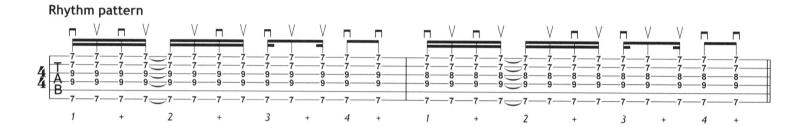

Rhythm pattern

Intro

Bm/F#   Bm(11)/F#   F#7sus4   F#7

F#m7   Gmaj13/F#   G6   F#7

F#

w/rhythm pattern

Bsus4   B   Bsus4   B

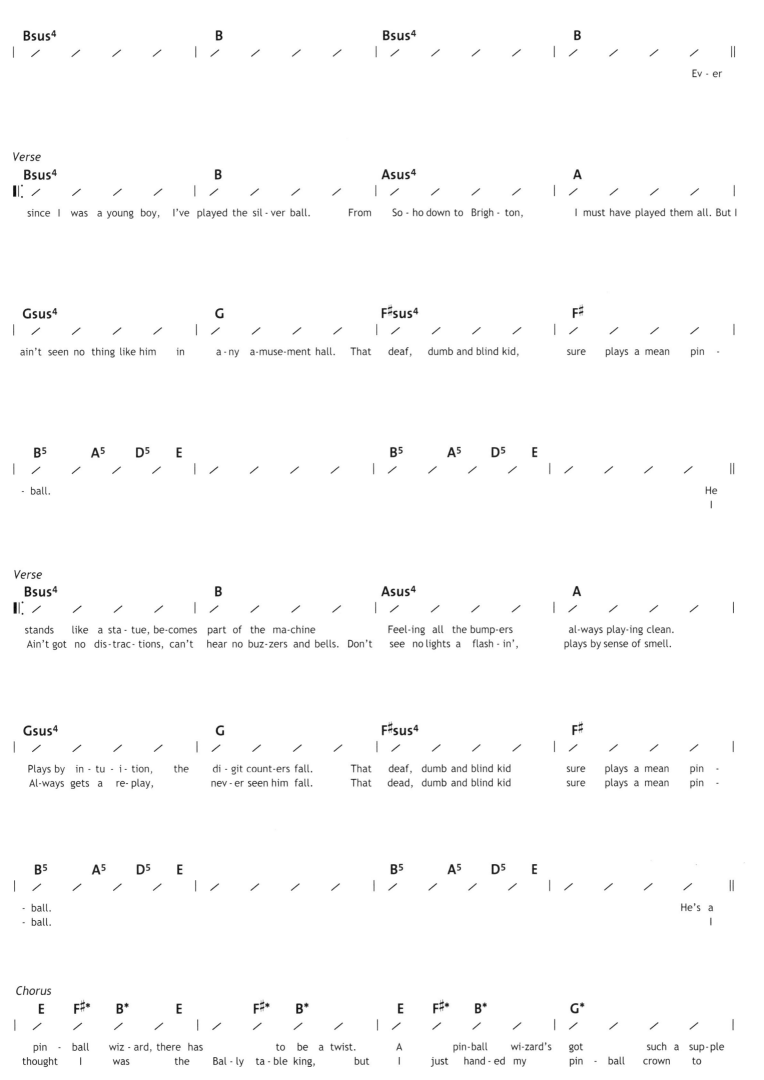

| **D** | | | **Dsus⁴** | | **D** | | | | |
| / | / | / | / | / | / | / | / | ‖ |

wrist.
him.

1.

Bridge

| **D** | | **Cadd9** | | **D** | | **Cadd9** | | **D** | | **Cadd9** | | **D** | | | |
| / | / | / | / | / | / | / | / | / | / | / | / | / | / | / | :‖ |

How do you think he does it? (I don't know) What makes him so good?

2.

Interlude

| **Dsus⁴*** | | | **D*** | | | **Dsus⁴*** | | | **D*** | | | |
| / | / | / | / | / | / | / | / | / | / | / | / | / |

| **Dsus⁴*** | | | **D*** | | | **Dsus⁴*** | | | **D*** | | | |
| / | / | / | / | / | / | / | / | / | / | / | / | ‖ |

Ev - en

Verse

| **Dsus⁴*** | | | **D*** | | | **Csus⁴** | | | **C** | | | |
| / | / | / | / | / | / | / | / | / | / | / | / | |

on my fav-'rite ta - ble he can beat my best. Has di - sci-ples lead him in and he just does the rest. He's got

| **B♭sus⁴** | | | **B♭** | | | **Asus⁴** | | | **A** | | | |
| / | / | / | / | / | / | / | / | / | / | / | / | |

cra - zy flip-per fin - gers, nev - er seen him fall. That deaf, dumb and blind kid sure plays a mean pin -

| **D** | | **C*** | **F** | | | |
| / | / | / | / | ‖ |

- ball.

Outro

| **B♭** | | | | | | | | | | | | | | | | | *Repeat to fade* |
‖: / | / | / | / | / | / | / | / | / | / | / | / | :‖

76

SPACE ODDITY

Words & Music by David Bowie

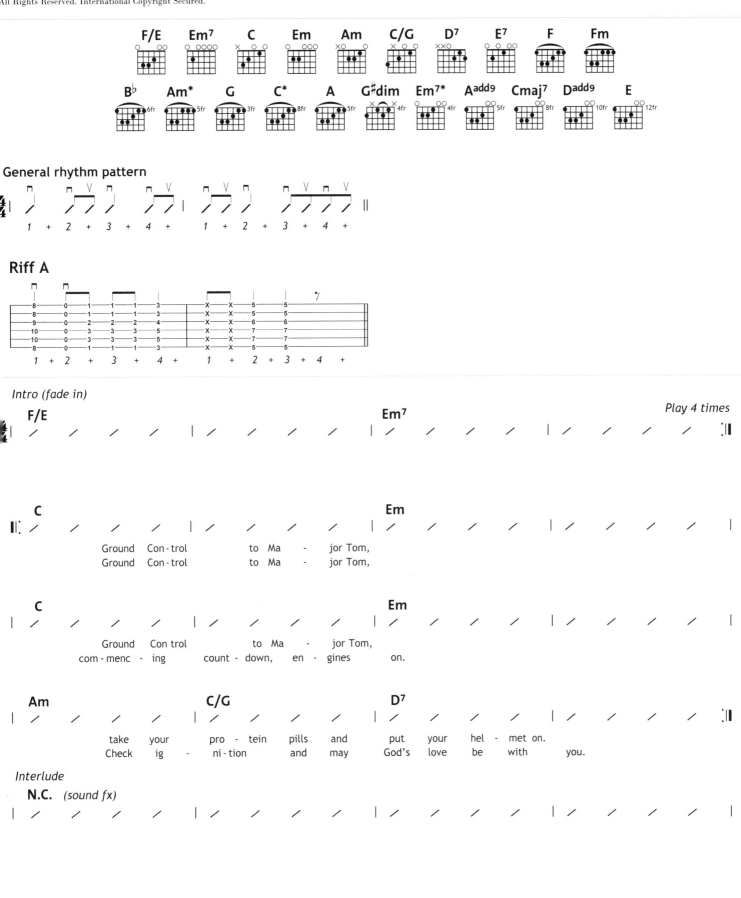

Verse

C / / / / | / / / / | **E⁷** / / / / | / / / / |

This is   Ground   Con-trol   to   Ma -   jor Tom,   you've   real-ly   made   the grade.
This is   Ma -   jor Tom   to Ground   Con-trol,   I'm   step-ping   through the door.

F / / / / | / / / / | **Fm** / / / / | **C** / / / / |

And   the   pa -   pers   want   to know   whose   shirts   you wear,
And   I'm   float -   ing   in   a most   per-cu -   li-ar way,

F / / / / | / / / / | **Fm** / / / / | **C** / / / / |

Now   it's   time   to leave   the   cap -   sule   if   you dare.
and   the   stars   look   ve -   ry   dif -   fe-rent   to - day.

1.   **F** / / / / | / / / / |

2.   **F** / / / / | / / / / ‖

For

𝄋
Bridge

F/E / / / / | / / / / | **Em⁷** / / / / | / / / / |

here   am   I   sit-ting in   a   tin   can,
Here   am   I   float-ing 'round my tin   can,

F/E / / / / | / / / / | **Em⁷** / / / / | / / / / |

far   a-bove   the world.
far   a-bove   the moon.

B♭ / / / / | **Am*** / / / / | **G** / / / / | **F** / / / / |

Pla-net   Earth   is   blue   and   there's   no - thing   I   can   do.
Pla-net   Earth   is   blue   and   there's   no - thing   I   can   do.

| / / / / ‖

Link

Riff A   **Riff A**

C* / **F** / **G** / **A** / | / / / / | **C*** / **F** / **G** / **A** / | / / / / ‖

Guitar solo

F/E / / / / | / / / / | **Em⁷*** / / / / | / / / / |

Aadd⁹ / / / / | / / / / | **Cmaj⁷** / / / / | / / / / |

Dadd⁹ / / / / | / / / / | **E** / / / / | *To Coda* ⊕ / / / / ‖

Verse

C / / / / | / / / / | **E⁷** / / / / | / / / / |

Though I'm past one hun - dred thou - sand miles, I'm feel - ing ve - ry still.

F / / / / | / / / / | **Fm** / / / **C** / | / / / / |

And I think my space - ship knows which way to go,

F / / / / | / / / / | **Fm** / / / **C** / | / / / / |

tell my wife I love her ve - ry much, she knows.

F / / / / | / / / / ‖ **G** / / / / | **G♯dim** / / / / |

Ground Con - trol to Ma - jor Tom, your

Am / / / / **C/G** / / / / | **D⁷** / / / / | / / / / |

cir - cuit's dead, there's some - thing wrong. Can you hear me, Ma - jor Tom? Can you

C / / / / | / / / / | **G** / / / / | *D.S. al Coda* / / / / ‖

hear me, Ma - jor Tom? Can you hear me, Ma - jor Tom? Can you...

⊕ *Coda*

Repeat to fade

E

‖: / / / / | / / / / | / / / / | / / / :‖

79

SPEED OF SOUND

Words & Music by Guy Berryman, Chris Martin, Jon Buckland & Will Champion

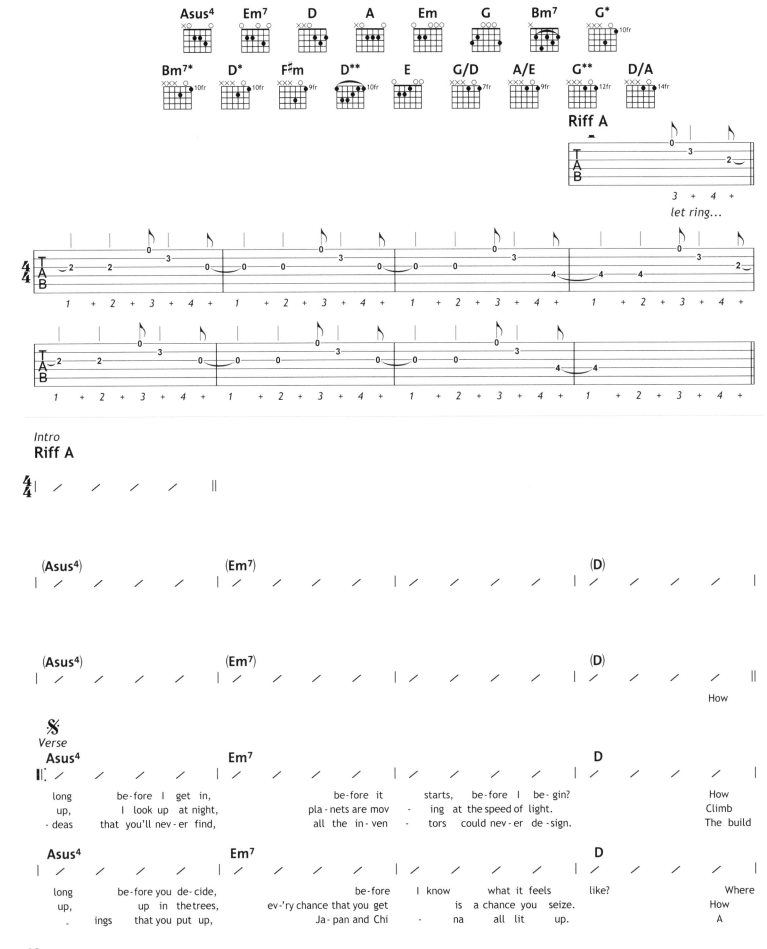

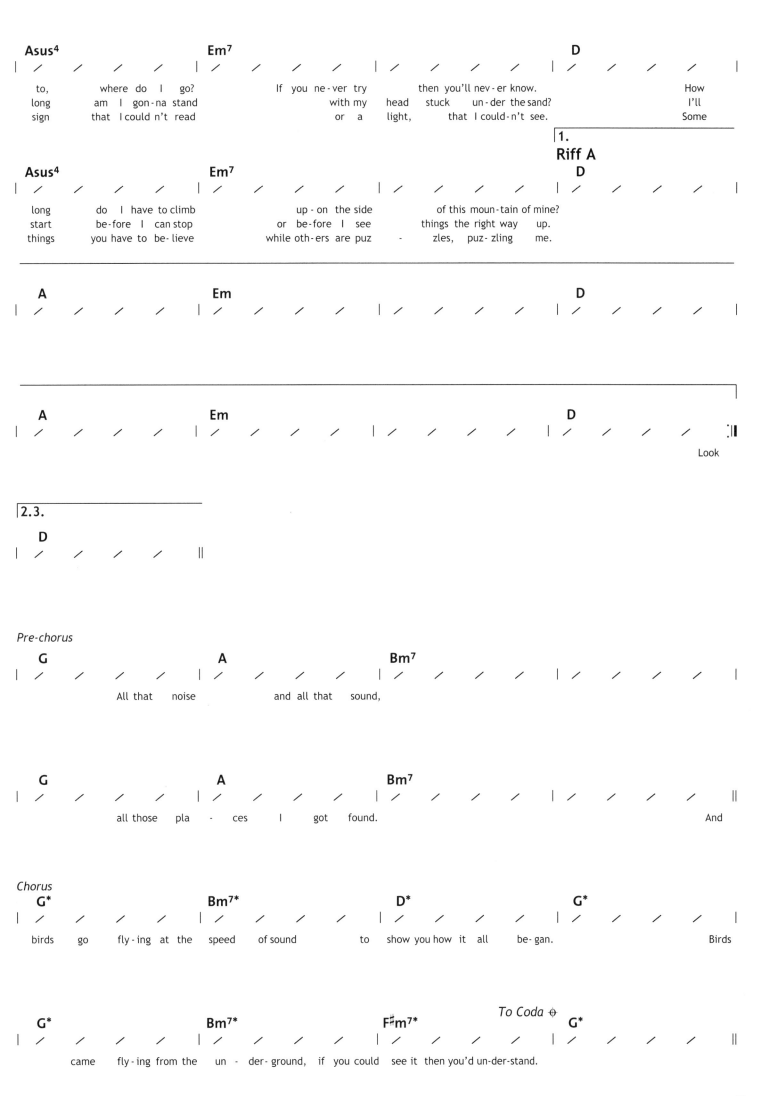

Asus⁴　　　　　**Em⁷**　　　　　　　　　　　　　　　　　　　**D**

to,　　　where do I go?　　　If you ne - ver try　　　then you'll nev - er know.　　　　How

long　　　am I gon-na stand　　　with my　head　stuck　un - der the sand?　　　　I'll

sign　　　that I could n't read　　　or　a　light,　that I could-n't see.　　　　Some

1.
Riff A

Asus⁴　　　　　**Em⁷**　　　　　　　　　　　　　　　　　　　**D**

long　　　do I have to climb　　　up - on the side　　　of this moun-tain of mine?

start　　　be-fore I can stop　　　or be-fore I see　　　things the right way　　up.

things　　　you have to be- lieve　　　while oth-ers are puz　-　zles, puz- zling　me.

A　　　　　　　　　　**Em**　　　　　　　　　　　　　　　　　　**D**

A　　　　　　　　　　**Em**　　　　　　　　　　　　　　　　　　**D**

Look

2.3.

D

Pre-chorus

G　　　　　　　　　　**A**　　　　　**Bm⁷**

All that　noise　　　and all that　sound,

G　　　　　　　　　　**A**　　　　　**Bm⁷**

all those　pla　-　ces　I　got　found.　　　　　　　And

Chorus

G*　　　　　　　　**Bm⁷***　　　　　　　**D***　　　　　　　**G***

birds　go　fly-ing at the　speed　of sound　　to　show you how it all　be-gan.　　　Birds

To Coda ⊕

G*　　　　　　　　**Bm⁷***　　　　　　　**F♯m⁷***　　　　　**G***

came　fly-ing from the　un - der-ground,　if you could　see it then you'd un-der-stand.

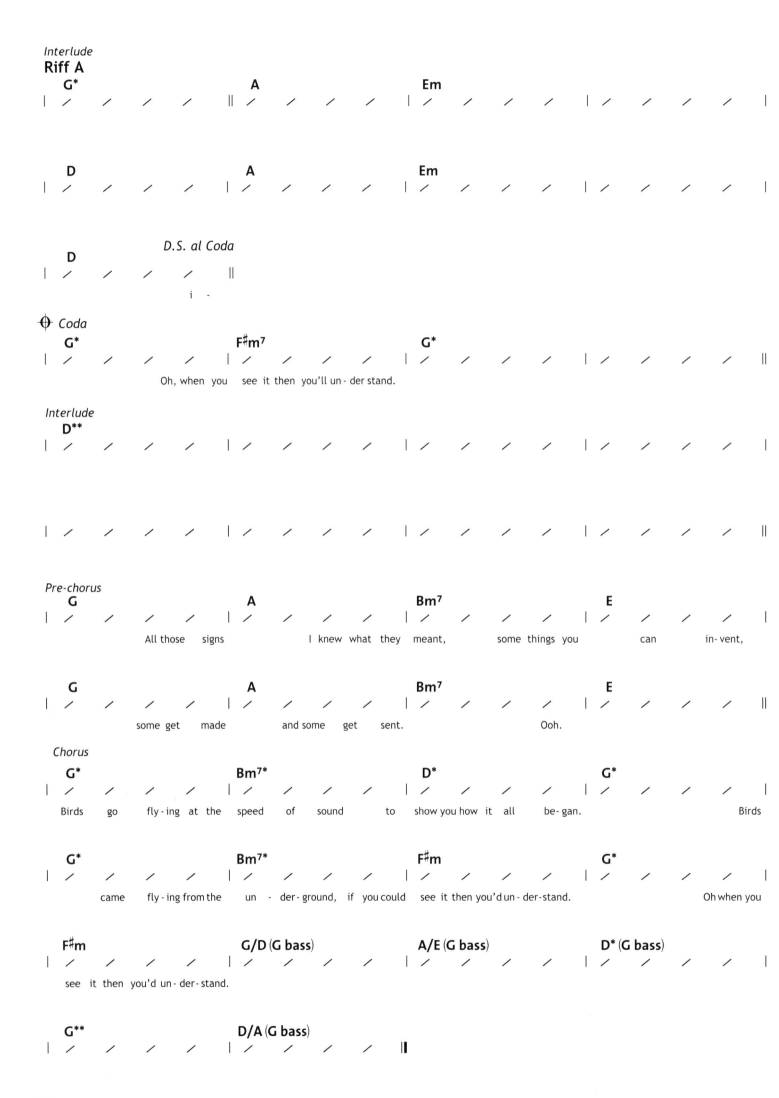

Interlude
Riff A

G* · · · · ‖ A · · · · | Em · · · · | · · · · |

D · · · · | A · · · · | Em · · · · | · · · · |

D · · · · ‖
D.S. al Coda

i -

⊕ *Coda*

G* · · · · | F♯m⁷ · · · · | G* · · · · ‖

Oh, when you see it then you'll un-der stand.

Interlude
D**

| · · · · | · · · · | · · · · | · · · · |

| · · · · | · · · · | · · · · | · · · · ‖

Pre-chorus
G · · · · | A · · · · | Bm⁷ · · · · | E · · · · |

All those signs I knew what they meant, some things you can in-vent,

G · · · · | A · · · · | Bm⁷ · · · · | E · · · · ‖

some get made and some get sent. Ooh.

Chorus
G* · · · · | Bm⁷* · · · · | D* · · · · | G* · · · · |

Birds go fly-ing at the speed of sound to show you how it all be-gan. Birds

G* · · · · | Bm⁷* · · · · | F♯m · · · · | G* · · · · |

came fly-ing from the un - der-ground, if you could see it then you'd un-der-stand. Oh when you

F♯m · · · · | G/D (G bass) · · · · | A/E (G bass) · · · · | D* (G bass) · · · · |

see it then you'd un-der-stand.

G** · · · · | D/A (G bass) · · · · ‖

STAY (I MISSED YOU)

Words & Music by Lisa Loeb

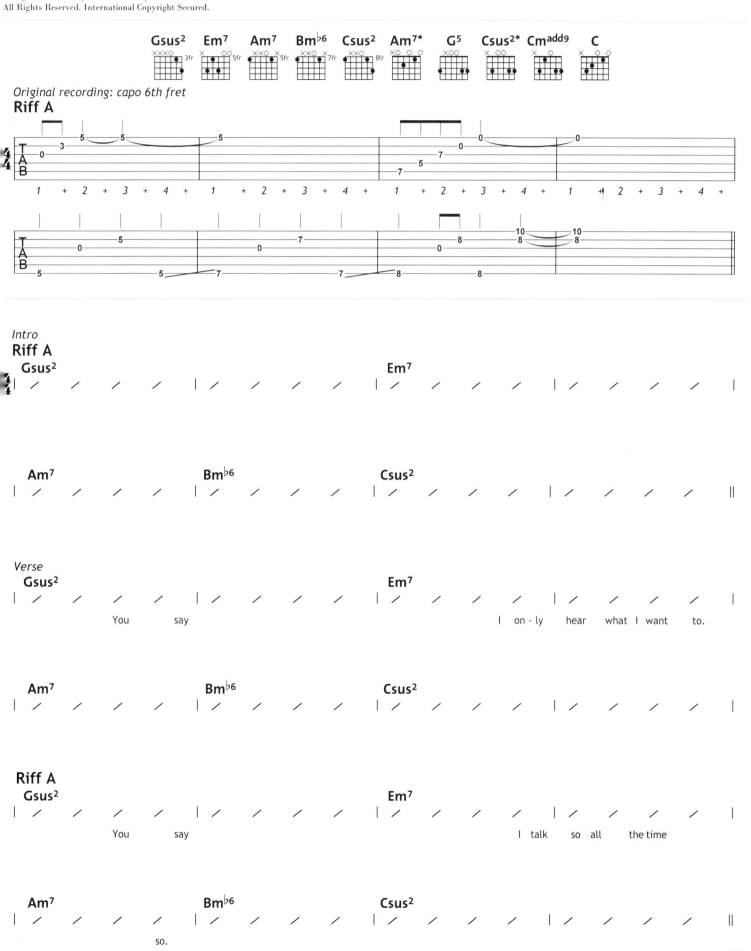

Original recording: capo 6th fret

Riff A

Intro
Riff A

Gsus²   Em⁷

Am⁷   Bm♭6   Csus²

Verse
Gsus²   Em⁷

     You   say   I on-ly   hear   what I want   to.

Am⁷   Bm♭6   Csus²

Riff A
Gsus²   Em⁷

     You   say   I talk   so all   the time

Am⁷   Bm♭6   Csus²

     so.

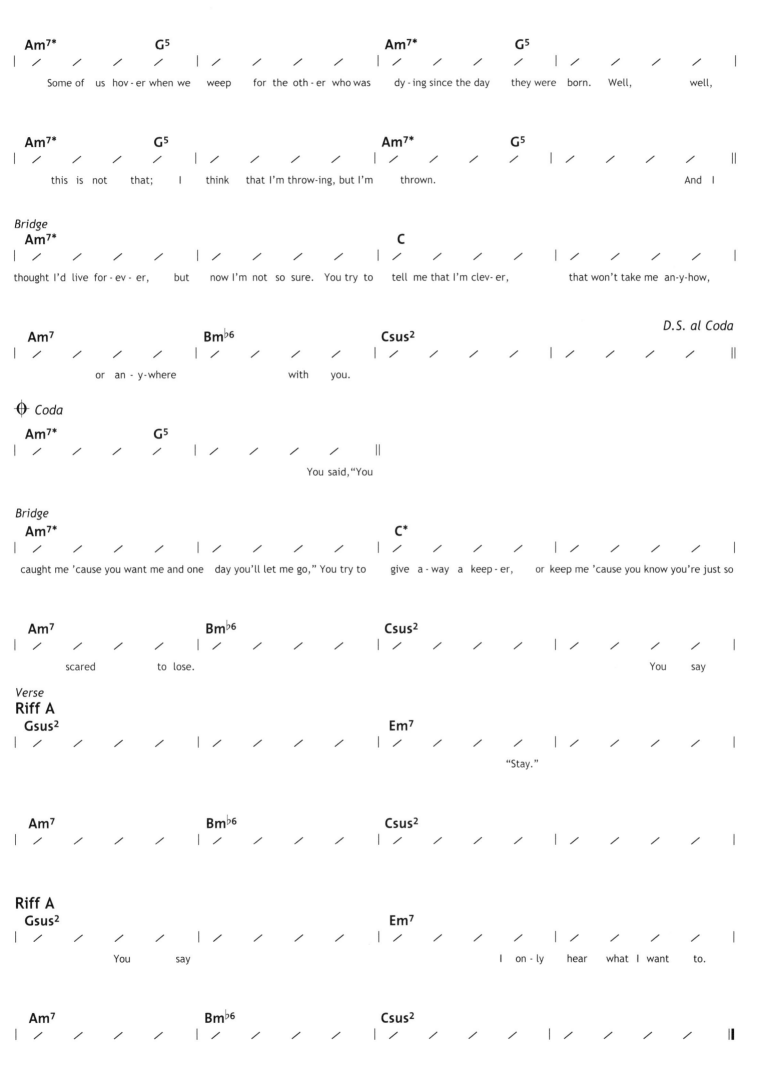

SWEET HOME ALABAMA

Words & Music by Ronnie Van Zant, Ed King & Gary Rossington

D   Cadd9   G   F   D5   C5   G5

Riff A

Intro
Riff A

D   Cadd9   G   D   Cadd9   G

Verse

D   Cadd9   G   D   Cadd9   G

Big   wheels keep on turn - ing   carry me home to see my kin.
Well I heard Mis-ter Young sing a - bout her,   well, I heard old Neil   put her   down.

D   Cadd9   G   D   Cadd9   G

Sing-ing songs a-bout the South - land   I miss A-la-ba - my once a-gain, and I think it's a sin, yes.
Well, I hope Neil Young will re - mem - ber,   a south-ern man don't need him a-round   a - ny how.

1.
Interlude

D   Cadd9   G   D   Cadd9   G

2.
Chorus

D5   C5   G5   C5 D5   C5   G5   C5

Sweet   home A - la - ba-ma,   where the skies   are so   blue.

D5   C5   G5   C5 D5   C5   G5   F Cadd9

Sweet   home A - la - ba-ma,   Lord, I'm com-ing home to   you.

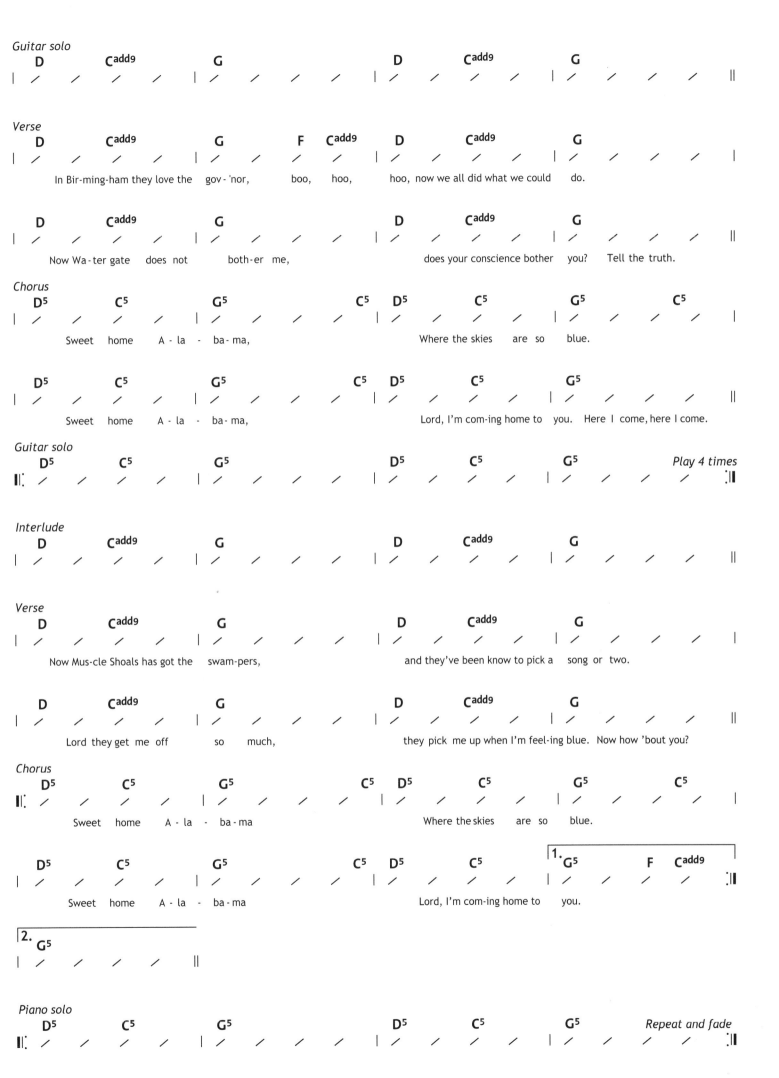

THERE SHE GOES

Words & Music by Lee Mavers

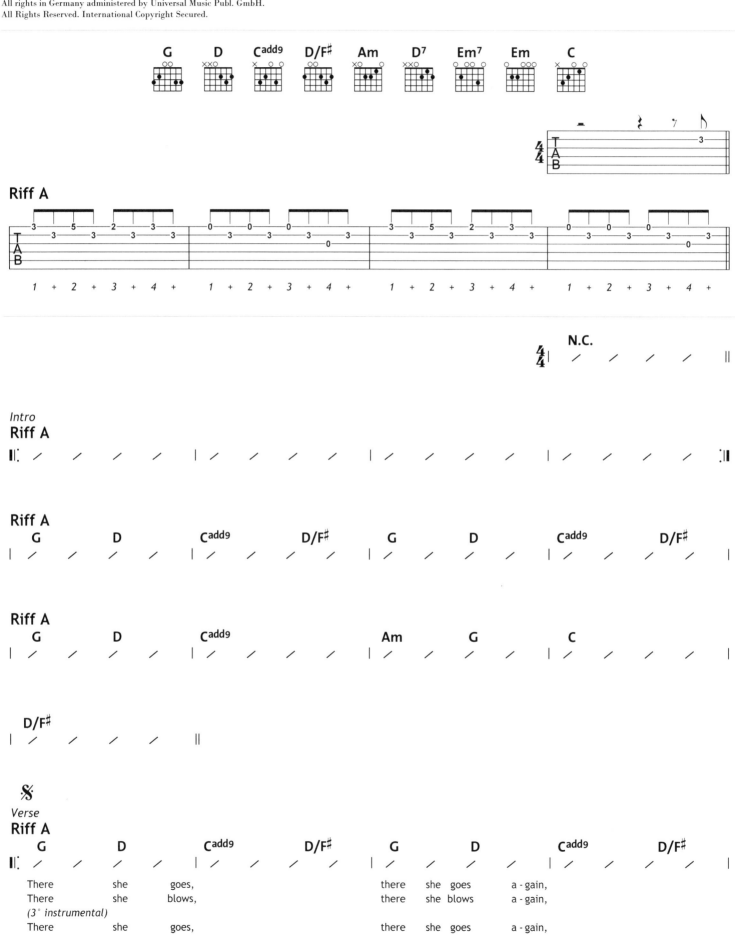

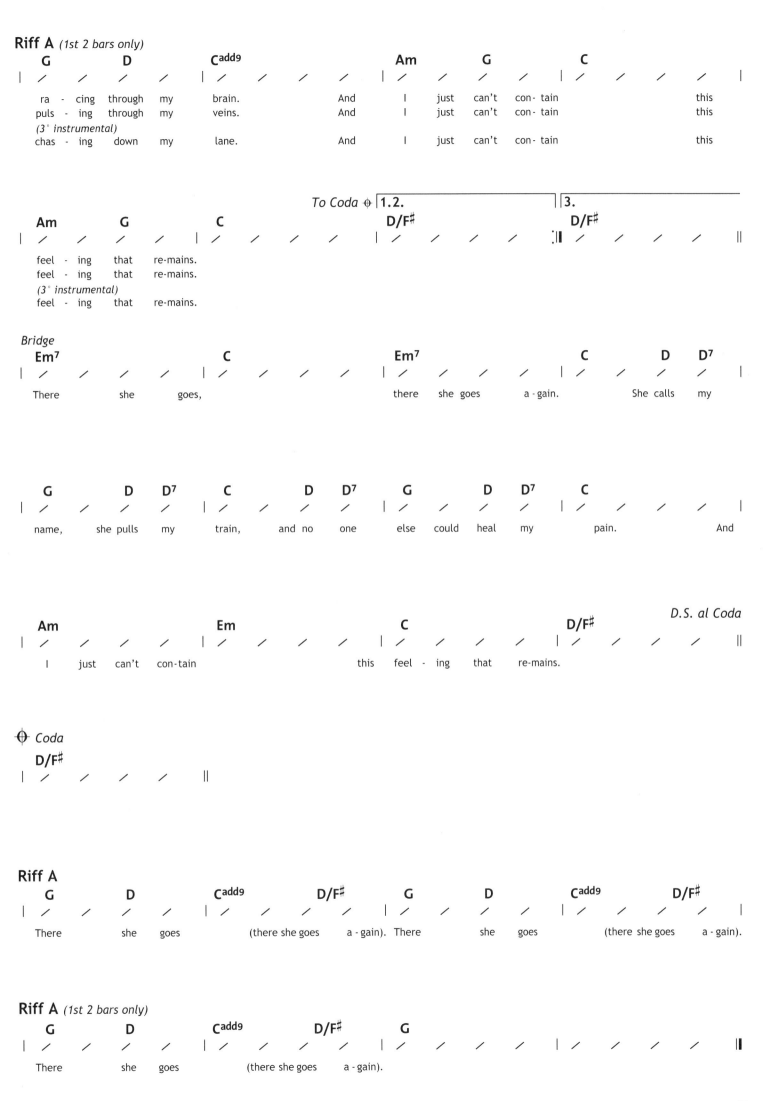

TIME AFTER TIME

Words & Music by Cyndi Lauper & Robert Hyman

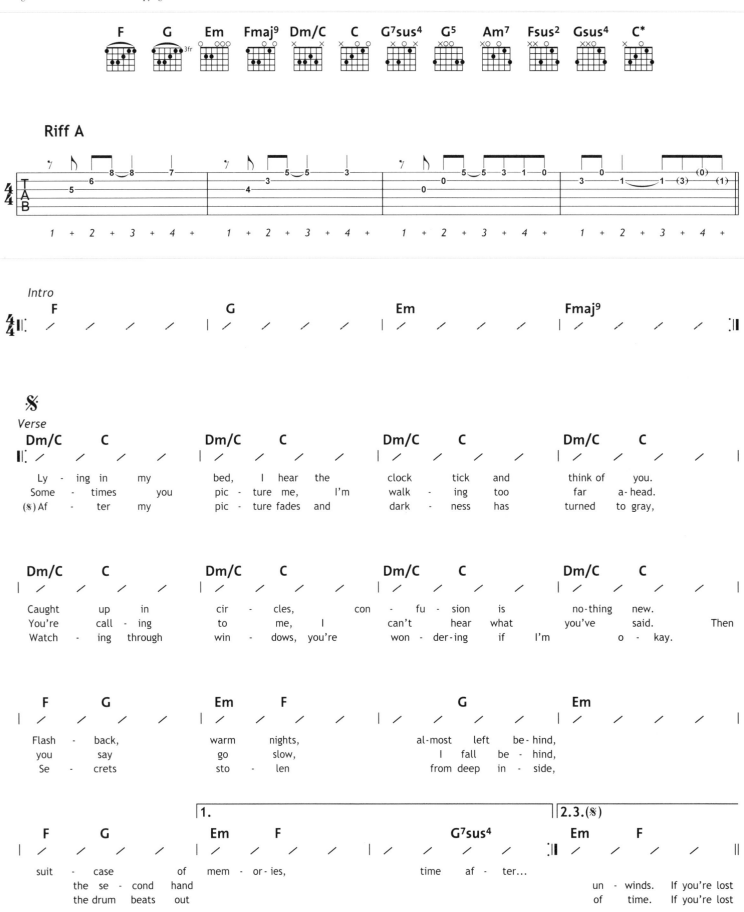

WALK THIS WAY

Words & Music by Joe Perry & Steven Tyler

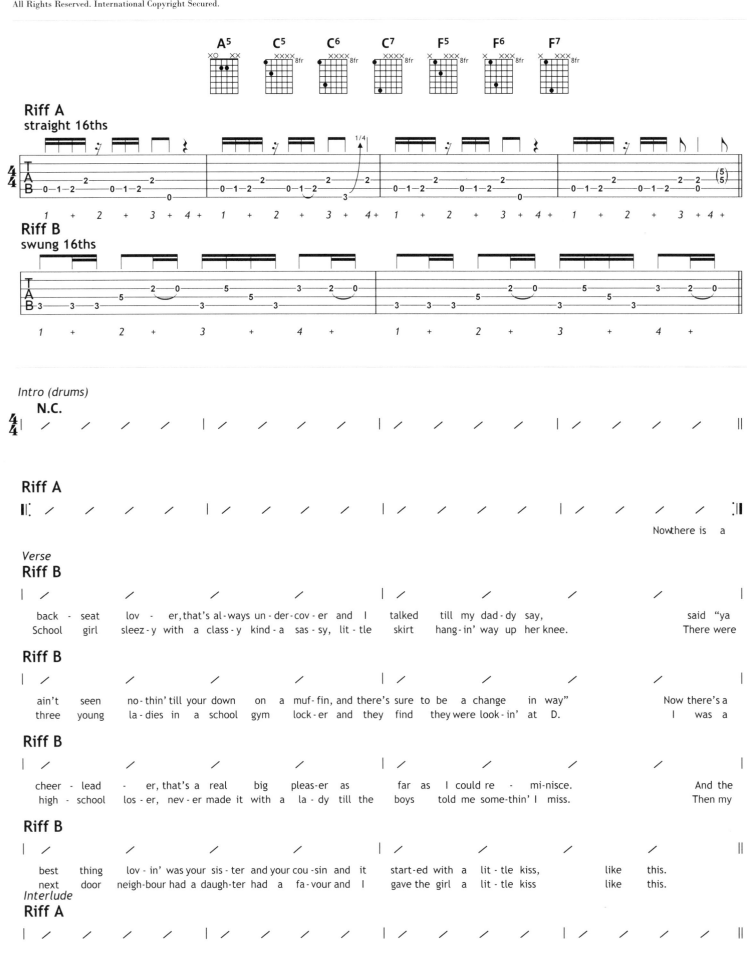

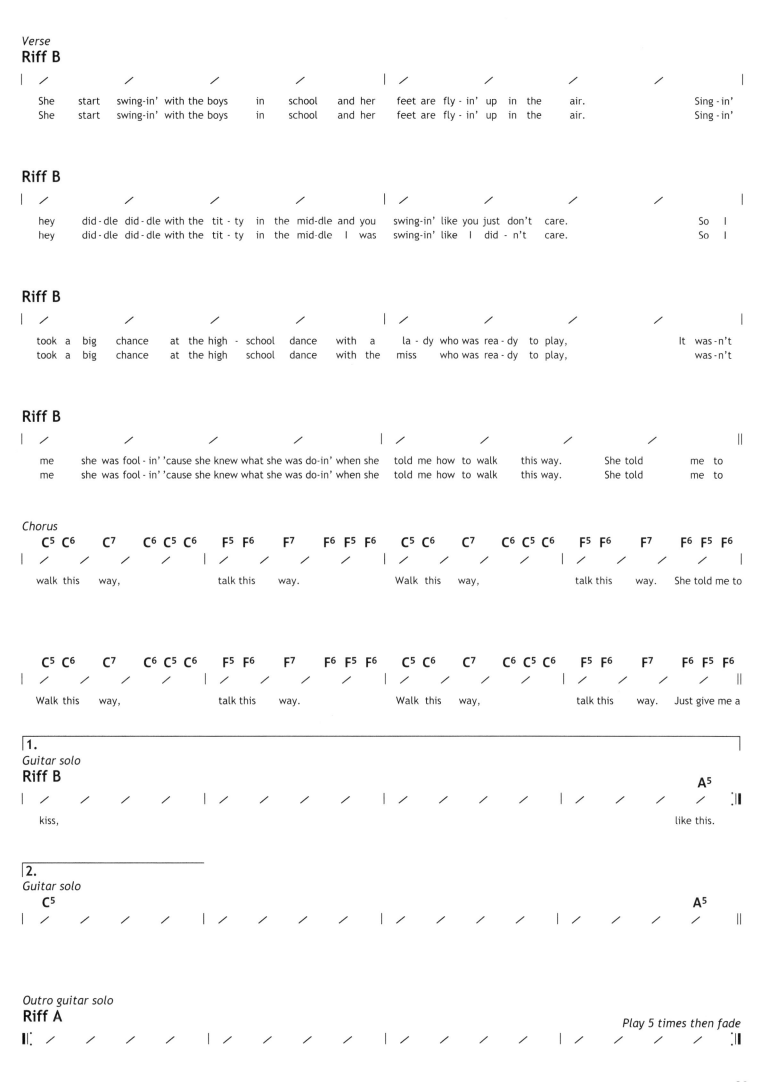

WATERLOO SUNSET

Words & Music by Ray Davies

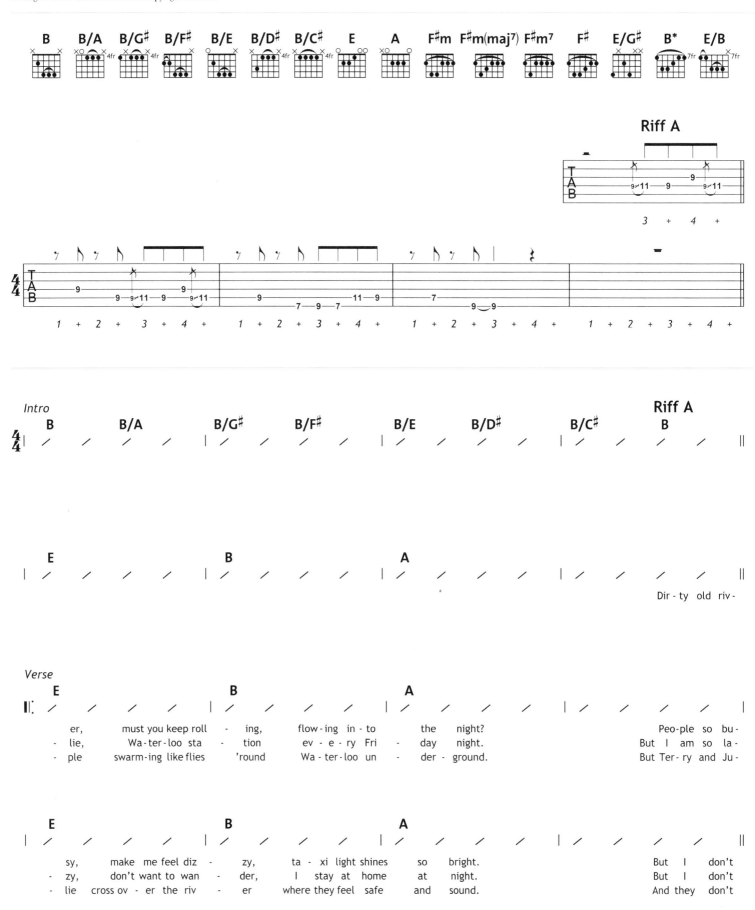

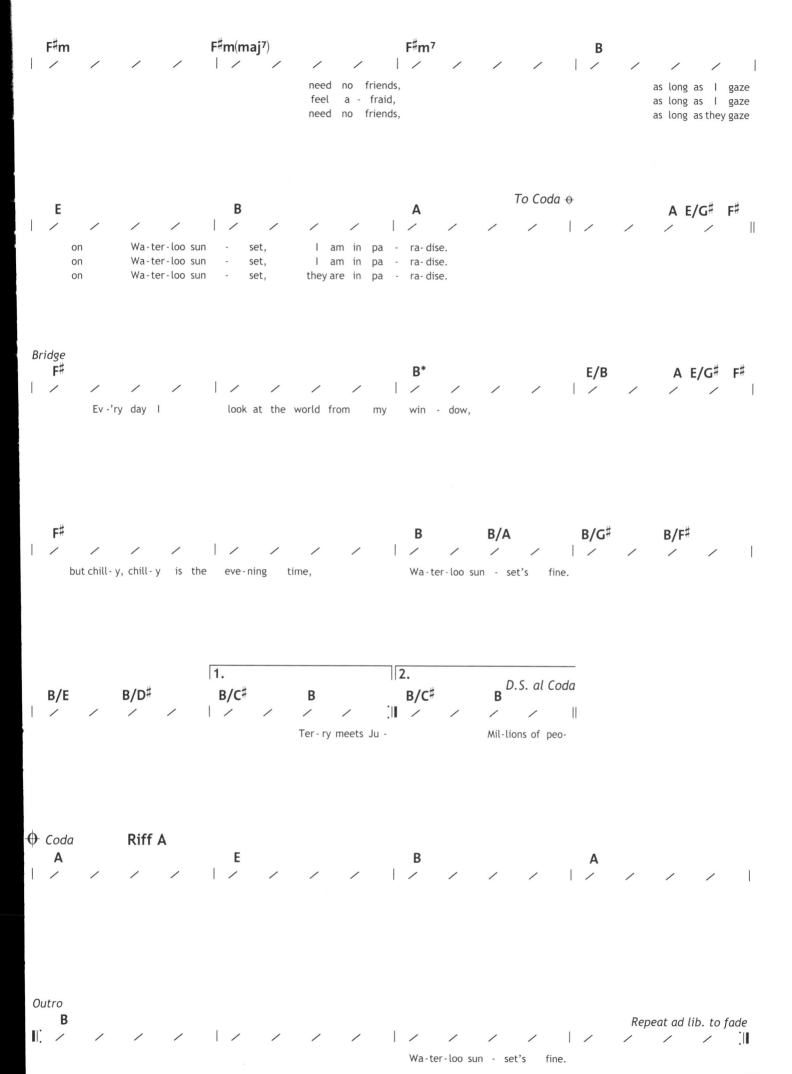

HOW TO USE THIS BOOK

Each song in this book is accompanied by a short segment of guitar tablature giving you an authentic, distinctive feature: an intro, a riff, a strumming pattern, a rhythmic figure, or other musical 'catch-phrase' to make your performance flow.

Watch out for instructions within the music – usually 'Riff A' or similar – to tell you when to play the notated figure. Sometimes, where it's more useful, a suggested strumming or picking pattern is included that can be used throughout the song.

Tablature (or TAB) is a system of notation specific to the guitar, and giving instructions not easily written in conventional notation. As with standard notation, rhythmic values can be indicated with note-tails and, in this book, the beat-count is also included below the staff to make rhythms easier to read.

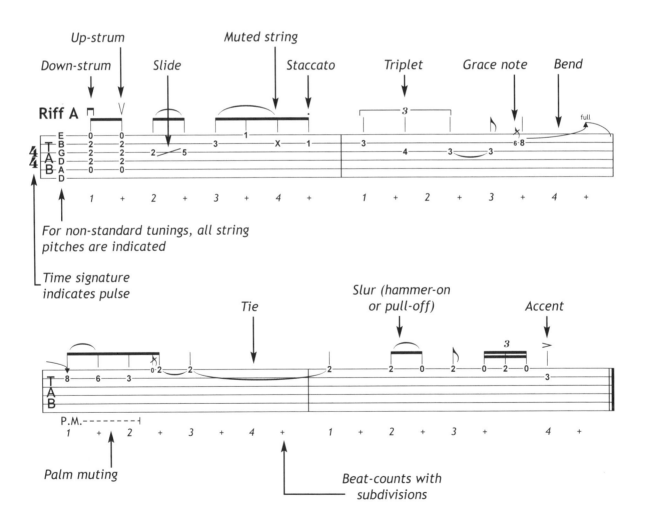